Robin Scott-Elliot was born E(
as a freelance journalist and tra......ng in Africa, he joined the
BBC in 1998 and later moved to ITV. He now works for the
Independent and lives in London with his partner and daughter.

the way home

Robin Scott-Elliot

Matador
9 De Montfort Mews
Leicester LE1 7FW, UK
Tel: (+44) 116 255 9311 / 9312
Email: books@troubador.co.uk
Web: www.troubador.co.uk/matador

ISBN 978-1906221-959

Typeset in 11pt Bembo by Troubador Publishing Ltd, Leicester, UK
Printed in the UK by The Cromwell Press Ltd, Trowbridge, Wilts, UK

Matador is an imprint of Troubador Publishing Ltd

For Iona

ACKNOWLEDGEMENTS

Many people have helped make this book happen and I am particularly grateful for the advice and assistance of Andrena Duffin, Chris Anderson, Adair Anderson, Allan Anderson, James Forsyth, John Lee, Celia Lee and, above all, the patience, support and encouragement of Karen Graham.

Extracts from *The Times* are reproduced with kind permission of Times Newspapers Ltd.

This is a novel about real people and real events

THE ANDERSONS

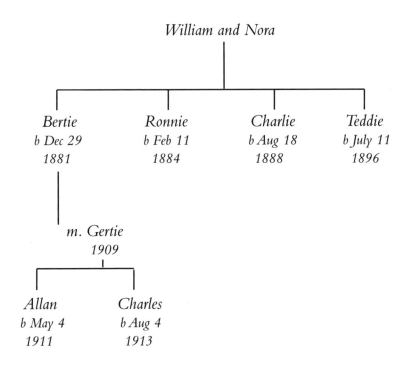

William and Nora

Bertie
b Dec 29
1881

Ronnie
b Feb 11
1884

Charlie
b Aug 18
1888

Teddie
b July 11
1896

m. Gertie
1909

Allan
b May 4
1911

Charles
b Aug 4
1913

CHAPTER 1

HOME

Ronnie, May 16, 1905
18 Woodside Terrace, Glasgow

My dear Teddie,

I hope you are having a good time and enjoying yourself.

Have you made many runs at cricket – the weather has not been very nice.

I hope you will get on well at the Sports. I won a prize at the Sports my first term, but never got any more.

Have you seen Charlie yet? I suppose he will be over at the Sports.

I hope you are learning to swim, and that you like the Baths. It is a very nice wee Bath at Cargilfield, and you will enjoy the Fettes Baths when you go there, they are much bigger.

Bertie went off to Drumhead yesterday. Uncle Cam came up in the motor for him but unfortunately it was raining.

I am to get a holiday at the end of May – and am going up to London in a motor with John Bell – won't that be a jolly ride, 405 miles.

With love from,
Ronnie

* * *

Bertie, July 21, 1909
18 Woodside Terrace, Glasgow

Dear Ronnie,

Well, I have done it. I am now a married man and write from this address for the final time. We returned from the honeymoon last night and have a further night here before moving into our new home. Won't that be strange? Mr and Mrs Anderson at home!

I am determined to inform you of every single detail about the day – whether you are interested or not, dear brother! It rained (Scotland does not change) but that had little influence over proceedings as the Gilmours had everything arranged to perfection. In truth it was all much of a blur, so many have a call on your time and we were constantly being whisked here and there with smiles fixed in place across our faces, part pure happiness, the remainder pure bemusement. I could not tell you with any conviction who was there, apart from everyone who mattered (with one notable exception!). At any rate, in your absence Charlie did a noble job as best man, altho' public speaking was obviously not something instructed by Sandhurst. It did not seem to matter. As always with Charlie his earnest smile was enough to win a laugh after another stuttering story, and his uniform lent him a splendid air. I never wore anything quite so grand in my weekend soldiering I can tell you.

The Boy Soldier cut a dash through Woodbank, Tuppie's quite taken I fear! He had a weekend leave from his battalion and then it was back to Montrose, where at least he is not too far from Strathairly. Tuppie is now keen to accompany Gertrude and I whenever we head east to Strathairly, in her new role as sister-in-law of course!

Mother spends more and more time out in Fife, she is keen to leave Glasgow and wants Dad to come out too and take more of a back seat at the firm. I fear it's a lost cause. The two of them just sat and beamed their way through the day.

Which is more than Little Ben did. Our youngest brother does hate to be upstaged and the roll of chief usher was little consolation I fear. Mother calling him Honey Bee within hearing of Allan Gilmour didn't lighten his mood either. Nor did Charlie and I win favour by calling him Little Ben in public – he considers himself far too grown up to answer to those childhood names any more! Poor Teddie, as he insists we must call him!

He was particularly envious of Charlie and his uniform, and at one point during the evening he announced that he intended to join the army as soon as he left school, but not in some 'awful infantry regiment'. He stayed till the bitter end tho', he's a sticker. I think Fettes will do him wonders, bring out the best and knock off the edges. Or send him to the other side of the world like it did to you, dear Ron!

So now you have a sister to contend with as well. I tell you, she looked a picture. I will send you a photograph we had taken outside the church with all the party, perhaps the happiest moment on a happy day (tho' we all missed you not being there). I know Gertie and I belong together.

We had a wonderful ten days up north, the Gilmour's gave us use of one of their lodges and we walked and walked, must have covered half of Sutherland. I also taught her to fish, but I don't think I made a very able tutor as we caught nothing between us. The motor back to Glasgow felt very arduous after such a glorious time.

Now Gertie has the house to organise and I have work to contend with again. It seems an age since I was last in the office. That is all going well, Norman and I are taking more and more off the old men. It leaves them to get on with their own favourite areas and gives us more of the day-to-day running of the company's affairs. Again happiness all round – it is good to write such a jolly letter. Not a cloud on the horizon.

Frank Donald and George Harvey both send their hearty best. I am trying to rope Frank into the young unionists, his livewire approach is just what we need in Glasgow. As for George, well he's still George.

What news from Canada? I do hope the fruit business is prospering. It never ceases to surprise people when we say you are a fruit farmer, not the occupation most would have chosen for you Ron.

I must close now. Do write soon and let us know your plans. Dad does worry about you, he would like to know you are on to something solid.

With much love,
Bertie
ps Mrs Anderson sends her regards to her new brother!

★ ★ ★

Charlie, October 14, 1912
Solon, India

Dearest Tuppie,

Thank you ever so much for another long letter and the photographs too. So good to see you all, and Strathairly too – a pity only that it was not in the flesh! It was silly of me not to bring any photographs out, I never even thought to do it. I do miss it all, tho' I suppose I have to learn to accept it. I chose to do this so that's that. At any rate, it is not as if I don't enjoy it. It is such an adventure, travelling all the way out here and then seeing such sights.

What an amazing country, and the heat, you would not believe how hot it is. Parading in full uniforms is quite a battle. I'm not sure the heat would suit you. It is ever so dusty too, when the company goes off on route marches we kick up great clouds of dust – any enemy would see us coming from miles off!

I have some news. I have been promoted to Lieutenant, the youngest in the battalion. They will have to stop calling me the babe of the regiment now! It has been terribly embarrassing to carry that label, especially at dinners when ladies are present and one of the captains will address me loudly as 'Babe' and turn me scarlet.

To answer your question, I am afraid I will not be coming home any time soon, altho' I should be due for a long leave in just under two years from now. I know it seems a long time, but you watch, it will fly by and before you know it I will be back in Scotland.

I have had one short leave here. Myself and Grant went up to the hills for a few days and away from the heat. They are very beautiful and we took long walks through the forests looking for monkeys and strange, colourful birds. The station we stayed at looked just like an English village and there were several officers from other regiments up there as well on holidays. None of us were keen to go back down to the camp. One of them took some photographs which he promised to send on and I will send some to you when I next write.

So for now it is back to the routine of everyday life in the army. Some days are arduous, some are just plain boring, but soldiering is still the occupation for me. I hear your brother may agree with me. Bertie wrote that Allan is thinking of joining the yeomanry. You should hear what the others here say about the cavalry, terrible things that I could not put in a letter. Do tell him he must never look down on us foot men!

Bertie's main news was that we are now each an uncle and aunt. Have you seen the wee Allan? You must tell me all about him. Have the couple changed since the new arrival? Bertie has always been terribly grown-up, suppose that comes with being the eldest, but now a father too. Mother will have someone other than Little Ben to dote upon now.

We have a brigade sports day at the end of the month. It is to be a huge affair with the final of company football and rugby competitions, athletic events and a finale of the tug of war. I am to take part in some of the running, something I haven't done since Fettes. I can see you smiling as you read, you are terribly cruel. This evening we have a practice for it so I must go to prepare.

Wish me luck and do write soon.

With all my love,

Charlie

★ ★ ★

Ronnie, March 3, 1914
Umtali, Rhodesia

Dear Dad,

I write with news. I am coming home. Whether that's good news or not I don't know! I assure you tho' Dad I am not in any trouble or difficulty. Now that is good news surely?

I plan to leave here in a month or so and will be back for the Scottish summer. I have missed them, I really have. The smells and most of all the colour, the greenness of Strathairly and all around. Would we be able to all go up to Loch Inver for a time? I do like it out here and I am prospering, believe me Dad I am, but it is Scotland I feel that suits me best, if only I could be sure of it and sure of what I want to do. I intend to take the journey and voyage to come to a decision and so when I arrive home you will have the news you want – I promise you that.

Whether to farm? They have made me so welcome out here and I can stay if I want to. They have found a temporary manager to take over the ranch while I come home but he will step aside when I return. I have not told them I might not be coming back. Is that terrible? I do adore the ranch life here, more so than the fruit farm in Canada. That did tend towards squishy tedium, and it was beginning to turn my hands purple. Here the life is so active, so physical and always challenging.

Any so, I face quite a journey to get home, altho' it's almost the reverse of coming out so I know what to expect. I find I am not a good traveller, I'm always keen to arrive, and I inevitably mislay tickets and the like. I do hope it goes smoother than coming out. I will get the train down to Cape Town from Bulawayo – I will ride there as it is still the easiest way to get about.

You should see me on board my steed. I'm quite the horseman now altho' I am told, when my esteemed colleagues have supped, that I strike a ridiculous pose in the saddle. That rather hurt me, but they say my legs are not to scale – even by Anderson standards. Apparently I look like a stork riding a Shetland pony! I refuse to believe it!

I intend to spend several days in Cape Town before catching the boat as it is a beautiful place and well worth exploring properly. One of the managers here has a friend with whom I can stay. From there I will telegram the details of my passage.

I am looking forward to getting back. So much has changed since I left. I am looking forward to seeing my two wee nephews, Bertie was proud in his letters and I am sure you and Mother are too.

I had a letter from Charlie saying that he is hopeful he will get leave very soon and be able to come home, altho' he said one must always guard against the whims of the military.

That helped prompt me into a decision to come back. It is something I have been pondering for several months now and at last I am acting. How like me I am sure you're saying.

It has been sometime since we were all at Strathairly together. More than six years by my reckoning. I only know Little Ben as a boy. How he must have changed. He writes excellent letters, full of his exploits and plans. What a young man he must be. Has he decided on his path? I suppose I will find out when I get back.

With Gertie and the boys and all of us back at Strathairly there will not be a moment's peace for you or Mother. I don't suppose you are looking forward to it one jot!

It is peculiar that I have rarely thought of the comforts of home – life is so constant here there is rarely the chance – yet writing this has sent me off into daydream after daydream. The sound of the motor crossing the gravel outside the house, the echo of conversation as people come into the hall and then in the evening the provocative smells from the kitchen. I miss Glasgow too. The bustle and motion of the city, even its greyness!

I must stop this otherwise I will write myself into a decision and announce it before everyone here.

I must not forget the splendour of this place. The space and huge horizon. Riding out as the sun comes up to reveal the land is a wondrous moment and certainly something one wouldn't find in Glasgow!

I do hope the business is progressing as well as ever. I am sure you and Bertie and the MacLeod cousins make quite a team.

Give my love to Mother.

I am so much looking forward to coming home.

Much love,

Ronnie

CHAPTER 2

BEGINNINGS

August 5, 1914
The Times, London

WAR DECLARED
NOTE REJECTED BY GERMANY
BRITISH AMBASSADOR TO LEAVE BERLIN
BRITISH ARMY MOBILIZING
 The following statement was issued from the Foreign Office at 12.15 this morning:-
 Owing to the summary rejection by the German Government of the request made by his Majesty's Government for assurance that the neutrality of Belgium will be respected, his Majesty's Ambassador at Berlin has received his passports and his Majesty's Government have declared to the German Government that a state of war exists between Great Britain and Germany as from 11pm on August 4.

★ ★ ★

Diary of Nora Anderson, August 15, 1914
Strathairly

It is sunny again today. It has been a fine summer. The mind plays tricks with the past, but even so I cannot readily remember one as warm. Now we are at war. That is why I am writing. I have never kept a journal, never even as a girl. I am not sure I ever thought it necessary, or all together a good thing. What is it for? We are all far too busy to spend time pouring over the past and bemoaning what might have been. It was Jean who said I should.

 I heard from her this morning. She is a dear, replying as quickly to

8

my letter. I feel a little embarrassed for sending it, but she seems in agreement with me, which is a comfort. I do not want my family to go to war and I know they all will. Even Willie would given half a chance – thank the Lord he is too old! I just wish Teddie, my little Honey Bee, were but two years younger. Bertie should be all right, as a father, but Ronnie and Charlie, especially Charlie, will have to face the good fight sooner rather than later.

I do hope my Teddie will not. Tho that is wishful on my part. As Emerson wrote: 'When duty whispers low 'Thou Must', the youth replies 'I can'.' And that youth will be my Teddie.

Jean knows. She knows what it is like to send a husband off to war. I will not send my husband. In his stead it shall be my sons. She believes that I should write. She says her journal calms her. It helps her through the days when it can be very lonely. She has always been a thinker, perhaps too much for her own good. Yet I shall try as she suggests. She wrote that I should put down in a journal anything that troubled me and it shall at once lift some of the burden. It may very well be only a slight aid, but an aid nonetheless.

I intend to try, and sent Lily down to the village to buy me this journal this morning. She made a good choice I think, nothing too showy like so many things are these days. She is sensible. Whether I shall have either the time or the inclination to write in it with any regularity remains to be seen.

Willie arrived this morning. He is to stay two days before going back to Glasgow. He said that the city is a spirited place at the moment. There are large queues of excited young men trying to join up. I think Willie looks at them with envy. Elsewhere everything is as it was. The shops are full and so are the streets, although Willie insists everybody seems to have an extra spring in their step. He thinks a quick fight may do the country some good. He is very manly about it all. He was very angry about stories in the newspapers of people purchasing large amounts of groceries in case there is a shortage. Willie says it is unpatriotic. Tho' a woman cannot but help worry and I have already sent Lily into Methil to bring home extra sugar and tinned food that will last a time. She also bought two further tins of jam as she does like jam. I thought it a little unnecessary, but said nothing as she seems alarmed by the whole business.

She is worried McCullum will have to go to war, but I told her he is too old and she must not worry herself. They have been with us for so long that I can speak absolutely plainly to Lily. I have told her not to mention the jam or tins to Willie.

Ronnie arrives this evening. He has told his father he is to join up, which may well be the first thing he has done of which his father absolutely improves. His time in Africa has not changed him. He is as flighty as ever. If only he could be more like Bertie, or Charlie. Charlie will be the first to go I fear.

I must see to lunch.

★ ★ ★

Charlie, September 1, 1914
Port Said, Egypt

Dear Mother and Dad,

I hope you are both well and received my telegram from Bombay. I am sorry I have been silent since, but it has been frantically busy and I have barely had a moment to myself – one of the costs of being adjutant I'm afraid. I have actually just ceased to be adjutant as of two days ago. As we are heading for battle I wanted to be back in my company and the CO has kindly let me return, so here I am.

We arrived in Egypt two weeks ago after 16 days at sea. I most certainly could never join the navy. I do not know how long we will be here for, but we have been told we are for France and are all desperate to get there. I know Bertie, Ronnie and Teddie will be too and I do hope they all join the Highland Light Infantry as well. I'm so glad we can all be in it together. What adventures we shall all have.

It was a stroke of luck Ron was home at the time. I presume Bertie will step straight back into uniform, I wonder what rank he'll be given? He might outrank me! And Little Ben will make a fine soldier I am sure. He was always telling me about his cadet exploits at Fettes.

As for me, well, India is now far behind. As adjutant it was I who actually received the order we were to mobilise. There was huge excitement. It was not a complete surprise as we had kept up with the European situation, altho' we were often a day or two behind so not all the battalion were in barracks and I had to send messengers hurrying out all over the place to call them back. That was on the eighth and the next day we had to get all the families on the move. They have all gone to Ambala, where they should be more comfortable until this is all over and we go back to Solon. I must confess I felt glad that I did not have someone to leave behind in India as who knows when we shall return.

The battalion marched for Ambala on the 12th, I was fortunate to be on the train with all the headquarters staff (now my adjutant perks have gone it's back on foot for me!).

At Ambala the whole battalion entrained – what a sight it was as we filled this train to bursting and trundled out of the station to the sound of the men singing and the sight of families waving excited farewells.

We had two days squeezed on to the train, stopping only in Baroda where everyone was grateful for tea and refreshments and a chance to stretch their legs, then it was on to Bombay where we embarked on the SS Sumatra. There an extraordinary thing happened. We woke the next morning to find the crew gone, all the wretched natives had deserted leaving only the British officers! So there we were a battalion of soldiers sitting on a boat off Bombay without a crew! The rest of the fleet sailed off without us, whilst we became sailors for the day until a replacement crew could be rowed out to us. It was not until shortly after one o'clock the following day that we set off after the rest of the fleet.

Conditions on board were not pleasant, certainly they were far removed from my trip out when I had my own cabin and we dined each night with the captain after a day spent strolling the decks. This time I was in a wee cabin with three others and our kit piled everywhere. There wasn't a space anywhere on the whole boat and once we got out into the ocean it soon became quite choppy. Dawdling on the Gertrude on Loch Inver was no preparation for this! We were all very glad when we sailed into Port Suez.

Earlier that day, as we had passed Aden, we had been informed our final destination was Marseille.

It will be odd being back in Europe again. The cold to contend with again! I can't remember the last time I felt cold, not a claim you hear from many Scots!

Please could you send me out one of those Baedeker guides as I think it might be terribly useful. Please also ask Bertie if he has a pocket-sized French dictionary or phrase book he could send to me. He might have some left over from his time in Tours and he won't need them when he comes out. He must also write to me and tell me all about France. I want to have a go at the language, I do so wish I had paid attention during French lessons! We were trying to remember some in the mess last night and not one of us could come up with anything at all convincing. I do not think my aunt's pen shall get us very far!

It was not until we reached Egypt that we were able to catch up with events in France and we have been trawling through the newspapers. We have read some terrible things the Germans have done in Belgium. Did you see that they burned down a church whilst the village inhabitants were at prayer? The Hun deserve what is coming his way.

Spirits are high in the battalion and everyone is terribly excited and keen to get there as soon as possible to play our part. Many are saying it will not last long. The old heads who served in South Africa say that modern warfare is sure to be short such is the weaponry we possess.

If it is all wrapped up good and quick – altho' not before we get there I do hope – I might be able to come home for a time. My leave was due and I should be top of the list when it's all over. It would be very handy if we were in France then as I could be home in no time, altho' knowing the Army they will ship us straight back to India, probably via Southampton so as to just show us a glimpse of England.

We reached Port Said, a chaotic town, two nights ago and have been sent out to guard various key points, like bridges and the wireless station. None of us are altogether sure what we should be looking out for but there is talk of spies.

I am writing this after lunch and we are about to take the men out on a route march. That is all we seem to do when not on guard duty. We are trying to make sure the men, and us, are all toughened up after that voyage so when we get to France we are ready to go straight after the Hun.

Please send my regards to everyone and tell them I will write to them all as soon as I have the time. Please send the books I asked for to me here as even if we have left they will be sent on after me.

Do also tell me all the news of my brothers, they have been so poor at writing in recent months.

With all my love,
Charlie

★ ★ ★

Teddie, October 19, 1914
Glasgow

Dear Mother,

Have you seen this morning's paper? I have done it. My commission is in the list from the London Gazette. I am now officially Second Lieutenant EK Anderson of the Highland Light Infantry! That makes three of us. I'm sure Ronnie will give up his ridiculous notions soon enough and complete the set. I doubt he will last in the ranks. What an odd fellow he has become in all his time overseas. He will have to salute me now when he sees me!

More good news is that we are to be moved to Dunfermline so I will not be far away for the time being. We wait there probably till we get the call to France. In the meantime I have to sort out all my kit. Two of us went to try and buy a revolver yesterday, but they are just too dear. The man said they had doubled in price since the war began. When we said this was outrageous he just shrugged and said it wasn't up to him. So neither of us bought one. It will have to wait till we are next paid unless you can make me an advance. It would be terribly useful as there is so much we need to have as officers.

Another of the new officers, a chap called McGregor, told me how it works. You can get it all here in Glasgow, but it is actually cheaper to send to London for it, or best go down yourself but I don't think there is any chance of getting the time to do that. So a group of us think we may get together and send for it all in one lot, get what we can afford and then see what's left and add to it as we go along.

I wonder what we will need for the front? I am sure there will not be room to take much. We will probably have much more of an idea once we get over there. It will be my first time out of Scotland!

It is great fun here, there are a couple of boys who were at Fettes with me. Most of us are new to the army, apart from what we did at school, and us and the men are all learning lots of new things.

I saw Dad yesterday at the kirk. He said he is ever so busy in town and does not think he will be out to Strathairly for sometime. You must understand Mother, with Bertie and Norman joined up, Dad and old Mr MacLeod have plenty to do. Most of their younger clerks have gone to join up as well, I think most of them are in the 17th with Bertie. Glasgow is as it always was. Everywhere is business as usual and everywhere is proclaiming it's 'Business as Usual'. There are men in khaki about, but many not.

Plenty have joined up and are waiting for their orders and uniforms, yet there are still plenty who haven't come forward. They are plagued by young ladies who hand them goose feathers in the street. I was walking through George Square on Friday morning when I saw a terrific set to between a man and three ladies. He was shouting at them that he had joined up but had been told to go home and await orders. They were shaking their heads at him and tutting in a way ladies twice their age would have been proud of. Poor chap, he didn't stand a chance!

They say that in the Western Isles there are whole islands without any young men left on them as they have all answered Lord Kitchener's call to arms.

It is going to be a tremendous time. I think I might make a career out of the Army. It suits me. I am going to learn to ride a motorcycle.

Give Lad a hug from me.

Love from,

Teddie

Ps Please don't call me HB in your letters, it would make me look very childish if anyone were to see it over my shoulder. I should be ragged to pieces.

★ ★ ★

Bertie, November 14, 1914
Troon

Dear Ronnie,

How is life with the Lovats? I wonder how you are taking to all this discipline and endless instruction. I await the day with great interest that I shall see you on a horse. Ron, I know you enjoy horses now and have become something of an expert horseman, but is being in the ranks how you can best serve when you are equipped to lead?

I have written in my pocket book a quotation from James Lane Allen. He wrote: 'Two heroic necessities make up a large part of our life; to be made to do what we dislike and to be withheld from doing what we desire'.

If ever there was a time when that held absolutely true then it has to be at this moment. When the call was for interpreters I stepped forward. I did it reluctantly as it is not what I want to spend this war doing, but if it is what is wanted then so be it. I was fortunate that they preferred to leave me with the battalion.

Ron, there is a shortage of officers, the Army is crying out for them and you must step forward. It hurts Dad that you do not. Do you read the newspapers? Do you read them saying that we have to step forward in this just cause? This is not something you can run from while you make up your mind Ronnie. Please go up for a commission.

If you have doubts look each day in the papers, see the lists of names that are beginning to fill the columns. Did you see Archie Graham died in France with the Gordons? Did you see the list of names from the Camerons who fell? There are names there that we know.

I do not like to take this harsh line, but if you could see how it is hurting Dad. Please stop playing your games.

Have you talked to Allan much? Gertie said her brother sees little of you. He also told her you would be most unlikely to get commissioned in the Lovats, but he would put in a good word with the Colonel for you and with his backing you would be bound to pick one up elsewhere. Come to the HLI. Think how pleased that would make Charlie.

I wonder where he is now. Have you heard from him? He may be in France already, altho' there was news in the paper that there are troops from India stationed in the New Forest so he may even be in England.

Life in the 17th is much as normal here by the sea. We at last are getting uniforms, altho' they are mostly blue and not khaki. We face endless rounds of drill and marching for at the moment there is little else we can do. The men are tremendous. Joining up all together has created immediate comradeship and I am sure Glasgow's men of commerce will not let the city down when we get out to France.

We actually went back to the city last week to parade. It was most odd at first, for when we marched out of the station great crowds were gathered but they made hardly a sound and we marched almost in silence to George Square. Suddenly when we turned in to the Square the crowd came to life and started cheering and cheering. In all it was a most peculiar experience.

I managed a Sunday at home after that, a chance to see the boys who seem to grow by the day.

I do hope all is well and please do think on what I have said.

Your loving brother,

Bertie

CHAPTER 3

THE FIRST

Diary of Nora Anderson, November 29, 1914
Glasgow

Willie told me this evening when he returned from the office that Charlie is in France. He may already be at The Front. An acquaintance of his in the city has a son in the HLI as well and he had a letter this morning saying they had arrived close to the line. I had hoped he might be kept in Egypt for a time. That would have been dreadfully disappointing for Charlie and much succour to me.

Willie says we should not expect to hear for a time. I suppose it will be once he has settled into life out there.

There have been some terrible letters in the newspaper from young men Out There describing what is going on. The papers do tend to speak in a military mind and it can be difficult to understand how the situation stands. Willie says he understands it all, although I am not entirely sure that he does. The letters speak of awful horrors, but the spirit is always strong. I cannot imagine receiving such letters from my sons, yet soon – very soon, it seems – I will be.

Gertie called for tea. The boys grow with every day and it was such a cheer to see their wee smiling faces. I can see their father in them. Gertie looked tired, I fear she finds it trying with Bertie away. They have always been such a close pair, so alike and so attentive to each other. They lean on each other. So this separation is going to try them. I did not know what to say to her and so we spoke of others. She spoke much of her sister. Tuppie is said to be beside herself with worry over Charlie. I wonder if this might finally make them declare an engagement, although I am not sure Tuppie would suit the life of an army wife.

I am writing more now that I am back in Glasgow. It unsettles me more here and I now feel I want to write this. I have not often written when at Strathairly, the country does suit me so much more. It is kinder to me.

There is also so much to do there. We have turned out the flower beds and planted them over to vegetables. Potatoes to the left of the house and carrots to the right. McCullum asked me whether I wanted him to dig up the lawn. I do hope it will never come to that.

★ ★ ★

Charlie, December 2, 1914
France

Dear Mother and Dad,

My it is cold. We were given European clothing when we landed but it is not nearly adequate and I shall have to send home for some warmer kit as soon as we know where we are going to be. I hope you'll be able to send me parcels. A warm overcoat would be an ideal beginning as the greatcoats we have been issued with are rather threadbare.

I write this as we puff slowly north across France. It is gone midnight and at last everyone is quiet and I can put pen to paper. I am wedged in the corner of what was a second-class carriage, but there is little of any class about it now. It is even worse than our cabin on the ship, with boots, bodies and kit everywhere. The air is thick but we can't open the windows and wouldn't want to either because of the chill outside. I can make out little of the countryside and we have no idea where we are heading. I don't suppose I would be allowed to tell you if I did know.

It seems to have taken us an age to arrive here. It is almost four months now since we left India and we were not happy being left on guard in Egypt whilst the rest of the division went on. After a time we feared we would have to stay there because of the threat from the Turk. Then at last we boarded ship again and after three days sitting in the harbour at Port Said we made for France. It was a journey that was at times alarming. There are Huns and other enemies active in the Mediterranean and we were on constant watch along with the crew, who at least stayed where they were this time! It was a relief to finally reach Marseille.

We anchored off the coast just before dawn and once the sun rose we went into the port. What a sight! It is as if all the world's nations (apart from the Hun of course!) are meeting in one place. There were soldiers and sailors of all sorts. C'est formidable (show that to Bertie!).

We disembarked and marched through the town, a great crowd gathering to cheer us along. French girls rushed out to link arms with the men. One corporal in my company, a particular dour wee Glaswegian who it is said had never been seen to smile, was beaming from ear to ear with a Mademoiselle on either arm. A word from the CO soon put that right and as the girls were sent packing, the comforting scowl returned to its rightful place.

Everywhere you look there are soldiers, and such colour. The French infantry wear red trousers and blue jackets, their mountain troops are submerged beneath great big berets called 'La Marmite' that flop down over the side of their heads. Then there are the cavalry, who came clattering through making a terrific racket. They look as if they have galloped straight out of a history book. The dragoons have great silver helmets and off the curved crowns flow a long black plume. They also wear silver coloured breast plates. I fear they will not do much to halt a bullet's progress. Our uniforms looked desperately dull in comparison.

They have troops from the north African deserts as well, Arabs wrapped in flowing white robes brandishing fearsome looking sabres. Ron would have thoroughly enjoyed the proud exhibition they made. It all makes for a splendid sight.

One French officer whom we met that evening said we can expect plenty more remarkable sights. He said the Belgiums [sic] use dogs to pull their machine gun carts. Can you imagine Lad doing that?! He also said the Belgium army still dress as they did when Napoleon was around. I am not sure they will be of much use at the front.

After we had marched through the town we were taken to a French army barracks to be quartered for the night. There we received our European uniforms. We have also been told we cannot take white handkerchiefs to the front for fear that we might use them to surrender. That was not well received by anyone as you can well imagine, but that is why there were women outside the barracks selling coloured handkerchiefs. Have you heard of this? Apparently it was in the newspapers. So 'Mouchoir rouge' became the first words of French most of the men learnt! It means red handkerchief.

It had been quite a day and I had to go back down to the docks with a detachment to help complete the unloading of all the battalion's equipment. I tried to use my new French on the dockers but they did not understand a word and neither did I when they replied. The sergeant lost his temper, something that never takes very long, and soon made himself understood in the language of the barrack!

When we were finished the transport officer and I were able to nip off to the Splendide Hotel for a drink before we had to go back to barracks. It was there we met this French officer. He has been to the front but would not tell us much. He said there was little point as it had all changed since the 'madness of those early days' and then clammed up good and firm. We have read about the retreats and no one is pretending we shall be off to Berlin at the double but he did seem rather gloomy. He brightened up after we bought him some wine. I asked him if they spoke the best French in Tours and he laughed. He wanted us to stay and dine with him but we had to get back to the battalion.

The next morning we marched back through the town where we boarded this train and this is now our second night on it. We have stopped a couple of times and have been allowed off for a few minutes but have to stay close to the train. There are soldiers everywhere, mostly still French but I think we are heading north to where the main British forces are.

Do pass on all my news and I will write when I can. Please send me a warm coat if you can. I have seen some good looking ones in the Times (it is a treat to see the papers again before they are absolutely past it) – perhaps you could ask Bertie what he thinks would be best? Nonetheless you must know that I am well and in excellent health.

All my love,
Charlie

* * *

Charlie, December 15, 1914
France

Dear Bertie,
I am in the front line! We came up four days ago after a week's

19

preparation behind the lines and are now being blooded. It is all rather grim but exciting too. It is mid-afternoon and all quiet so I have the chance to write.

I am sitting on a small box just outside the entrance to my dugout. Down there it is warmer but the air is rank, up here is cold but I can at least breathe and the men can see I am not cowering down below, which I think is important.

I thought I would write to you first before Dad as you will be following me and are best served by knowing what it is like out here and can pass it on to our brothers. Please also pass on my love to Tuppie and tell her I am well and thriving and will write to her as soon as we are settled into our routine. It seems as if we get mail pretty regularly and I am told our letters reach home at a decent rate too, which is better than the slow boat from India.

On the way up we actually came through Orleans, which I am sure you know well from your time at Tours. We were on that train for an age and I would be quite content to never see one again. You can rely on the Army tho' as they soon gave us the chance to find our land legs again with a 10-mile march to our billets.

As we left the train we were issued with a half sheet of what the Army calls their French dictionary. It would make you laugh. It is of little use, but the officer who was in charge of something or other at the railhead told me the high command feel they have to do something as there has been confusion from the very top down.

Apparently when the Expeditionary Force first arrived in France, they hardly had an officer who could speak French and the French had few competent English speakers amongst their headquarters staff. He said the confusion of those early days had to be seen to be believed. He was a friendly chap and very talkative.

He also told this story of a group of English officers being entertained in a restaurant in Boulogne by a tubby French officer (a lot of them are rather rotund it seems), who was holding forth in his stumbling English about the magnificence of the Republic's army.

'They would follow me anywhere. It would not matter if I led them with a rifle or a tartine,' he proclaimed and the table fell into silence. After a deal of embarrassment they at last they established that tartine is the dish of bread and butter that they provide for you in restaurants here, rather than anything more literal! That's just a wee amusement, but you can surely imagine the confusions that have arisen whenever we collide with our glorious allies.

The next few days were fairly intense as we made ready to go to the front. We were a few miles back, billeted in a large farm house and its outbuildings – I had a bed of straw that was extremely comfortable after the torture of the train.

For the first time it was possible to hear the front. It was like a rumble of approaching thunder, like in India when the monsoon was on its way, vaguely menacing but still distant enough to keep a man curious.

It looks like the monsoon has struck here as it is ever so wet and the mud gets everywhere, absolutely everywhere. You could not imagine. It is impossible to stay clean or dry. I look down at my boots and they are covered in mud and it reaches up my trousers, everywhere is flecked with light brown sludge, my hands and face are streaked, sometimes it feels like we shall never be dry again. If I was a wee boy I would be in heaven. I think my greatcoat is probably doubled in weight such is the thickness of its covering.

It was a few mornings ago that we moved up to the front here at La B_____, in the region of the town of Albert, which I think you know. It was surprisingly peaceful and we got in swiftly up the support trenches to the front with little incident.

It all seemed rather unreal, as if you were watching yourself from above. Occasionally there was the ziiiing of a bullet passing which is alarming at first but you soon become used to all the different noises. That entire day was pretty quiet as we settled in and completed the hand over.

It didn't last and the next day the Hun welcomed us to France. We were shelled and lost three men wounded. They were all from the neighbouring company so I didn't see any of them. When the shelling begins we all take what cover we can inside the trench. Some head for the handful of dugouts we have.

There are a couple of 'deep' ones, altho' that's only down a few steps into a small, dark and damp chamber. The others are little more than scrapings into the side of the trench. I prefer them as they protect you from any shrapnel and I don't fancy being buried below in one of the deeper ones.

As for the one where I live (when I have to), there is a pool of water on the floor which acts as our underground weather vane – when it rises it is raining outside! Sandbags have been thrown down to try and create some sort flooring but the water is still winning. Around the sides are several ledges which you are able to squeeze on to try and sleep. In the middle there is an upturned box on which we have set up our stove and keep a candle alight. I will try to spend as little time as possible down there, it really is foul and gloomy.

One's first shelling is an intense experience. When it finished my first thought was relief that I hadn't funked and I believe you could see that in all the men's faces as they smiled at each other once we crept from our shelter. It felt like our baptism. Now we really are soldiers.

When we first came in I must confess to nerves, yet I suppose one is bound to be wary of the unknown, whether it is swimming out of one's depth for the first time or going to war! I am a soldier tho' and it is what I chose to become. Anyhow, the flutters soon passed as they always seem to.

The next day was quiet. We stand to before dawn as it is then that the greatest threat is, but once that has passed we have breakfast and begin our duties. So far that has meant trying to improve our conditions. Have you ever tried to dig in mud? It wasn't a very fruitful day.

Yesterday turned out to be rather warmer. All of a sudden around midday the enemy bombed part of our trench and forced our men out of it. We bombed them back whilst the trench was repaired and late in the afternoon we were able to move back in. There has been more activity today. Last night the Indians, who are next to us, were forced out of a sap and a patrol led by Grant had to try and re-occupy it today. They were bombed by the Hun and couldn't manage it and Grant was wounded. He was taken back to a casualty station but I think he should pull through.

It is all very different, so different to everything I have learnt in six years as a soldier. India's been my be all and end all for the last few years and there is very little, if anything, I learnt there that can be applied here. I have learnt more in four days here than I had previously in my entire time as a soldier.

It is all quite confusing really, for all of us, but it is a terrific adventure and terribly interesting, even though we live the life of rabbits, burrowing beneath the earth and then coming out when it is quiet. At night there are always flares going up to light up the sky and they mix with the bright flashes of explosions to make quite a show – as long as you are not on the receiving end!

Teddie badgered me in his letter to tell him what he should bring. I will write out a list to send him, in the meantime anything warm and waterproof would be good. Another good idea, which I would like someone to send out for me, is an air cushion. The officers that we relieved when we came up all had them and said they could not get by without them. I will write fully on all this when we complete our spell in the line. I am not sure how long that will be, but by then I shall really know what is useful and be able to give you a complete description of everything out here. Wouldn't it be grand if we could all be out here together!

I will end now as it is beginning to get dark and I must get the men ready to stand to. Please write soon.

With all my love and Christmas greetings (in case I do not have time to write before),

Charlie

★ ★ ★

December 21, 1914
The Times, London

ALLIES ADVANCE
HEADWAY MADE ALONG THE LINE
Paris, Dec. 19

The following official communique was issued at 3 o'clock this afternoon:
IN BELGIUM – In the region of Albert in the night of December 17-18 and during the day of the 18th we advanced under a very violent fire and reached the barbed wire defences of the second line of the enemy's trenches.

The following communique was issued at 11pm: – The British troops have lost in the direction of Neuve Chapelle some of the trenches taken yesterday; while the Indian corps have advanced some hundreds of metres towards Richebourg-L'Avoue.

December 20
This afternoon's official communique says:-

The Allied forces got possession of a part of the German first line trenches along the front Richebourg-L'Avoue-Givenchy-La Bassee. The Germans attacked us twice very violently in an attempt to recapture the trenches taken by us on the 18th. They were repulsed.

The following communique was issued at 11 o'clock to-night:- No change has been reported to-day on the whole front.

GERMAN WAR NEWS
SUCCESS CLAIMED NEAR LA BASSEE
The following war news is officially circulated by German wireless stations and received by the Marconi Company:
BERLIN, Dec. 19

Main headquarters reports as follows: On the west front the enemy ceased his unsuccessful attacks upon us. The attacks near La Bassee were beaten off with heavy loss to the enemy, and 200 coloured and English prisoners fell into our hands and some 600 bodies of English soldiers lay on our front.

★ ★ ★

December 26, 1914
Post Office Telegraphs, London

To: Mr Anderson, Strathairly, Largo, Fife
Regret to inform Lt CH ANDERSON reported missing in Action December nineteenth.
From: SECRETARY WAR OFFICE

★ ★ ★

Capt J Inglis, December 27, 1914
France

Dear Mr Anderson,
I am sure you will have heard the terrible news about Charlie. He was reported missing on December 19th during the battalion's first

engagement in France. I wanted to write to tell you what happened and give our sympathies at your loss. I apologise for having taken so long to write but we have been frightfully busy.

I replaced Charlie as adjutant and always knew it was going to be a difficult task to follow in his footsteps.

He was not only able at his job but well liked, always with a smile on his face. He was popular with officers and men alike and the battalion have suffered a great loss, altho' I know it is nothing compared to what you have suffered.

He is reported as missing and whilst we cannot be certain after the confusion of the 19th, it was a terrible muddle of a day, I'm afraid it does seem likely that he has lost his life. It remains to be confirmed but I would not want to offer you false hope at such a terrible time. It is a time which calls for the utmost honesty.

Allow me to pass on to you the little I can of the day in question. In the morning we launched an attack on the German lines which was at first successful. Charlie was in the second line to reach the enemy trenches.

Unfortunately they became cut off there and were exposed to heavy German attacks throughout the day. When they were able to retire to our lines at dark Charlie was among those missing and no-one could say what had happened to him. That is the truth of the engagement, and the truth of the situation now.

It was my privilege to have known and served with Charlie. Our thoughts are with you and your family at this terrible time.

Do not hesitate to write to me should you have any questions and if I find anything more I shall contact you at once.

In deepest sympathy,
Capt J Inglis,
1st Battalion Highland Light Infantry

* * *

Diary of Nora Anderson, December 31, 1914
Strathairly

Oh, Charlie, my sweet, dear boy. Where are you?

CHAPTER 4

WAITING

Bertie, January 8, 1915
Troon

Darling Gertie,

Just a note to let you know I'm back with the battalion.

Still no news of poor Charlie. My hopes were raised by a report in the newspaper that some of the attacking Indian force from the day after his show have turned up as prisoners of war in Germany.

Every day in the paper there are corrections to the casualty lists. Just the other day I saw a Lieutenant Barry from the HLI (it didn't say whether he was the first or second battalion) changed from missing to prisoner. Captain Inglis's letter to Dad mentioned the confusion. He cannot have been sure what Charlie's fate was. I am sure we can only wait, yet I worry for Mother, and Dad too. It is a terrible strain. I wish they would stay at Strathairly but Dad will not let his work drop. He is doing so much for the Red Cross which is useful and needed but it does leave Mother rather on her own.

How is Tuppie coping? I was never sure how close those two were, Charlie was always very guarded in his letters.

It was a blessing to have some leave during all this horror. The boys are growing so quickly, especially wee Charlie. It is not a time one wants to be away from home.

I returned here to find that we have moved billets. The new one for C Company is even better. I have a sea view now. Otherwise there is little news.

We know we will be here for a while longer until the battalion is properly trained and considered ready to go overseas. Before that it is likely we will move somewhere down south for a time.

Life seems remarkably pleasant here, if occasionally a little dull, and one is loath to complain about anything after reading Charlie's letter again and the descriptions that appear in the newspapers. They have been publishing some very particular letters from men serving at the front. I wonder if he was frightened?

We have spent the last few days marching endlessly up and down the sea front, which when the wind is up is some battle. Then we march out of the town and practise digging trenches. It is not much of a challenge. We are still short of kit and weapons so have yet to spend much time on the range. Indeed we appear to spend more time parading for various dignitaries down from Glasgow, which provides pleasant interludes but is hardly the job to hand. Yet the spirit is excellent and the men are extremely disciplined. There has yet to be a single charge of drunkenness in the three months we have been here; the Guard Room is always empty and this in a seaside town which is not short of its attractions.

If any news comes of Charlie I will be sure to telegram you at once.
Your loving husband,
Bertie

★ ★ ★

Diary of Nora Anderson, January 14, 1915
Strathairly

I remember when he first went away to school. He was smiling. I imagine him in my mind and it is with that radiant grin lighting up his handsome face. Imagine him in your mind's eye and he will be smiling, I am sure of it. He was always the happiest of the boys, earnest but happy and he laughed as if every moment he stood on this earth, every breath he took, was a joy to him.

I worried for him sometimes. Everyone thought he was always happy so there was no need to worry about him. Mother said that if you go through life with a smile on your face then life will smile on you. He did have happiness in his short life. We were a happy family. Not always, of course. That is an impossibility, but this was a home filled with laughter. For him it must be so again. I demand it. For my dear, sweet boy.

I want to be able to bury my boy. It is a mother's right, is it not? I wanted to say that to Willie, but he will not hear. If I try to bring up the subject he will leave the room. The boys tiptoe around me in their letters, as if trying to offer me some Hope.

They all tiptoe around me. Yet they need not, indeed they should not for I know He is Gone. I can feel His presence elsewhere. Miracles do not happen in Scotland. I only want to say goodbye.

★ ★ ★

Ronnie, February 2, 1915
Gosport, England

Dear Dad,

So it is done. I do hope you saw my gazette – 2nd Lt AR Anderson. I wish Charlie could have seen it. He did so want us all to be in it together. At least now we are all in the HLI. I am sorry he will never know. I have also written to Captain Inglis asking if I might be attached to the 1st battalion as soon as they need their number strengthened.

For the time being I am here with the 13th, although there is talk of us being moved back to Scotland, which all would welcome as Gosport is not somewhere that holds a great deal of appeal. There are so many soldiers here and the town is just a mass of khaki. The weather has been awful, making everyone short-tempered and irritable.

Rain, rain, rain. One of my fellow officers claims it is all the gunfire in France that has affected the atmosphere and caused it to rain all the time. I consider that absolute rubbish; he does believe every word he reads in the newspapers and they do write such rot at times.

I suppose you will want to know how I did in my exams. All I will say is that I passed them all and can now officially read a map and know the make-up of a division. After what Charlie said I imagine most of one's learning will come in a hurry when one gets out there.

Life now is an early parade, another parade, endless drill and then a solid route march. We did 15 miles yesterday. That was when I longed for my horse. My fellow officers all seem a decent bunch, one or two odd ones, but then that is no different to Fettes or Rhodesia.

How is Mother? Bertie wrote she is bearing up well but longs for news.

I will send this now as I have to attend a course on 'advancing under artillery fire'.

With love,

Ronnie

★ ★ ★

Bertie, March 16, 1915
Troon

My darling Gertie,

This wait is interminable. By now surely it must be known. Ronnie wrote to me that he accepts Charlie is gone and it would be better for us all if we did the same. Sometimes Ronnie really surprises me. He is the family's flitter, never sure of what he wants or where he wants to be, forever leaving a confused trail behind him. Yet on this he has a steely conviction.

Remember Richter?

'Recollection is the only paradise from which we cannot be turned out'.

I keep thinking of Charlie. It is over six years since I last saw him and the thought that I will never see him again weighs heavy. It is another dull day here and from my window I look out over the sea and to the horizon where the grey ocean collides with the grey sky and we wait and wait. It is so cruel to have to have this hope. Yet one cannot give up on him. Surely whilst there is a chance he might have come through we must keep a measure of belief, no matter how small? It is one's duty to hope.

Yet we all know that is at best the slenderest of hopes. We all know that it is most likely that Charlie is gone. So we continue wrestling with this wait and rejecting the probabilities; fighting for peace of mind.

One's mood is not improved by reading the papers, nowhere is there solace to be found. Did you read General French's dispatch for December in the paper the other day? I poured over it, searching for any detail that might lend some understanding. For a time I did feel a degree of comfort in at least knowing what happened on that day, but then the questions started advancing and there are, of course, no answers to bar their progress.

When I go out I will, as you ask, be absolutely truthful with you. I will tell you every detail if that is what you want. I believe you are right that knowing the truth makes it easier for those left behind.

I have made Ronnie promise the same for when his time comes. He seems sure it will be soon. He has been bombarding all and sundry with letters urging that he might be sent to France. The HLI have been suffering and are short of officers after Neuve Chappelle. He will certainly go out before I do and probably before Little Ben too.

I have not shared my thoughts on Charlie with Teddie, nor have I mentioned to him about telling all when he does go out. I hate to see him touched by this. He is still so keen, so full of life and so determined to get on with it. I feel loath to stand in his way or to try to temper him. If anything Charlie's fate has made him even more determined.

The Scottish Unionists have suffered two blows of late. I'm sure you will have heard James Bell's fate. Our company was at Ayr at the time. They had just begun the parade on the racecourse when he fell to the ground and was dead before anyone even reached him. He was only a little past 40. Also George Smith has been killed in France with the Gordons.

Life here goes on, it's a remorseless routine of drill, route marches, musketry and digging. I do have one piece of news. The battalion has reached its full strength and so a new E company is being formed. I am to be second in command of it, again to Bill Auld. It is to become the battalion's reserve company when training is complete. What it means for me I am not altogether sure. It is likely that the company will remain behind when the rest of the battalion moves south. That moment is approaching as we are nearing the end of training. I do hope to stay with the battalion but it does seem unlikely.

My darling, I hope you are in good health and the boys are thriving too. I agree that you should leave Glasgow for the time and go back to be with your Mother and Father at Woodbank. Do take a trip to Strathairly in due course as Mother would so like to see you and the boys. Your visit would be a very welcome one in these times.

Your loving husband, B

* * *

Teddie, May 18, 1915
Dunfermline

Dearest Mother & Dad,

I am now a full Lieutenant!! My promotion came through yesterday and will be gazetted soon. I will tell you when so you can look it out in the newspapers.

I have also learnt to ride a motorcycle, they really are tremendous fun and I have decided to begin saving to buy one when the war is over. They get you around so much quicker than a slow old motor. When we get a decent spell off duty a couple of us borrow 'bikes and head off into the country.

Last weekend we went up to Montrose to watch the Royal Flying Corps squadron as Harry has a friend who is stationed there. It was thrilling to see the machines at close quarters and watch them going through their paces. Harry's chap is going out to France very soon. He says he is lucky as he will never have to go into the trenches like we poor old infantry. He said we should transfer to the RFC as they are in need of new flyers. I intend to speak to my CO about it.

Did you see Wyndham Halswell has been killed? Do you remember him? He was the pride of the first battalion. Charlie wrote of him a great deal as he was his company commander when he first went to India. He won the gold medal at the quarter mile in the Olympics. You probably won't recall the race. They had to run it again after a deal of barging in the first race, the Americans were furious and refused to race so Halswell ran the course on his own!

I see Ian Hamilton is commanding in the Dardanelles and the older, married chaps here say that a wife can always get her husband to do as she wishes. Mother, could you write to Lady Jean saying I am ever so keen to go out? Perhaps he could get me out there.

It is becoming very dull here. We are all ready to go and it seems such a waste to keep us all cooped up here. We undertake endless courses on this and that, it's worse than school! When we are not confined to the classroom we are off on long marches through the country. I am tempted to one day to march my men straight to Strathairly and spend the afternoon sunning ourselves on the lawn!

One joy is getting on the range. We get on a great deal now and I am the best shot in the company. We have tremendous competitions.

There is a Sergeant from Ardrossan who is a fine shot, he's an old regular who served in South Africa (he keeps us amused with endless tales of chasing the Boer) who had left the army just a few months before the war began. He re-enlisted at once and was made a Sergeant straight away as he had been a Corporal. They sent him to us to make sure we are not all novices. The other good shot is a Private from Firhill. He had never held a rifle before he joined. He was an apprentice carpenter. I think he shall be our company sniper. That's a terribly important job.

Dad, thank you for your letter. I am glad your Red Cross work is coming on. Our CO said it is terribly important work.

I am due a weekend pass before the end of the month so will hopefully get to Strathairly.

love from,

Teddie

★ ★ ★

Ronnie, May 22, 1915
Malleny, nr Edinburgh

My Dear Mother and Dad,

A very quick note to tell you I will be following this letter! I am coming home for four days because then I am for France! At last I am being transferred out there and am to join Charlie's battalion. When I saw the casualty lists from Ypres I knew my time had come and I am ready for it.

I am to leave on the night train from Edinburgh on the second and travel to London and from there straight on to Folkestone where I take the boat to France. I plan to spend four days with you at Strathairly then I will meet the two other officers who are going out with me to have a day in Edinburgh purchasing extra kit and provisions that we have been told will come in useful at the front. Then I have to come back here to collect the draft of men we will be taking with us. There is much excitement in the camp I can tell you.

I will leave here early on Saturday and hope to be at Strathairly by early afternoon. Could you collect me from the station? I will let you know the train.

Until Saturday, with all my love,

Ronnie

Diary of Nora Anderson, May 28, 1915
Strathairly

Ronnie left an hour ago. I didn't go to the station. I hope he did not mind. Willie's gone too so I am alone. He's going on to Glasgow and he wants me to follow tomorrow, but I don't think I shall. I want to stay here at my dear Strathairly.

Ronnie was full of war. He and his father talked endlessly of the campaign and talk of a big push to strike a 'hammer blow all the way to Germany'. They spoke of the government too. Ronnie said it was a good thing the Liberals were gone but Kitchener remains as the shortage of shells was not his error and it occurred to me that I have never in all his life heard Ronnie talk of such serious issues. Before all this he would sit at the table and chuckle when such talk began, trying to provoke his father or elder brother – which usually had the result he wanted.

He was such a frustrating child. There was always the feeling that he could achieve so much more if only he would put his all into a situation. Report after report from school would make the same claim. His father would be furious and Ronnie would plead with me to calm him down. It was always difficult to say no to Ron.

We were alone for a time yesterday morning. I was seated at my dressing table when he knocked quietly on the door. Oh Mother, he said, I don't want to let Him down. I said to him that he would not. I said that he must not consider such things. It cannot do any good. I fear now I was over harsh with him. He came looking for his mother and I wasn't the mother he wanted. I wonder if this war has changed me. I fear it will change us all.

He will be in France any day now and it will start again.

I am not going to go back to Glasgow. This is my home and this is where the boys know home. I wonder if we shall gather here again after the war is finished. I would like that.

If they could see it now. It is a scene with which they are so familiar. Everything is so green. I can hear the birds singing, but I can also hear the silence of the house with only the faint ticking of the clock in the hall. It is comforting and I always used to savour moments of quiet here, when the house was still. It felt like I was resting with the house. Now the silence is not such a comfort and there are days when I long for the sound of life and to hear voices echoing up from the hall and the sound of heavy footsteps bounding up the stairs.

I have Lad to keep me company but he does miss Teddie and spends much of the day sitting expectantly by the front door waiting for him to come home. He will sit up, head cocked to one side as if the door will be flung open at any moment and Teddie will come bouncing in. Of course, if anyone does come up the drive he will jump up and down and bark with excitement and wag his tail furiously. McCullum has to hold him back as he opens the door and then poor Lad, one can see the disappointment in his face. Then he will lie in the corner of the hall, next to the clock, feeling sorry for himself but still keeping an eye and an ear on the door.

I have much to do today. The clock needs winding. McCullum says we can have up some of our vegetables and then Lily and I are to make a large broth to take down to the village and serve to those that need it at the school.

I also must write my letters and I promised Ronnie I would knit some extra thick socks for him. He said it would make him think of home when he wore them. Mother, he said, I know now Scotland is my home. Strathairly is my home.

We hope Teddie may come home this weekend. I think Bertie has told him I need company and must be looked after. So our dashing lieutenant has asked his regiment if he may come home for Saturday night. It is not far and he is hopeful of being allowed. Bertie says that Teddie will only go out if there is a big push and many casualties result. The newspapers are certain that there will be one later this year. Bertie says we must have a push to win the war. Yet if there is a push Teddie and even Bertie may have to go out as well.

There have been long, long lists in the papers these past couple of weeks. Especially from the Scottish regiments. I have stopped looking. One keeps seeing names and thinking of mothers. The grocer in the village has taken to posting the most recent list in his window. Not everybody can buy a newspaper, but that is surely no way to discover a loss, before the gaze of your neighbours as sometimes the telegrams do not arrive in time. I intend to ask Mr Todd to stop the practice.

It has started raining. There is still no Other news.

CHAPTER 5

FRONT

Ronnie, June 11, 1915
France

Dear Mother and Dad,

I hope this finds you both well. I am in excellent shape if a little damp! I have been out here nearly a week now and all that time has been spent at the front. I arrived at lunchtime on the fifth and that evening we went into the line where we have been ever since. I suppose one has to be out here to realise the true gravity of the situation yet it is not nearly as bad as some would have you believe. I have yet to fire a shot.

So, I'm here, responsible at last Dad, and with much to live up to. Everyone says great things about Charlie. I am not in the same company, but have had a chance to speak with men from his company. It was a great comfort to hear what they said about him.

Like all things to do with the dear, old Army our life out here is all one of routine and once accustomed one soon slips comfortably into it. To begin with tho' it was all terribly confusing and I had very little idea what I was supposed to do. Still it was a relief to get to the battalion and be received by some friendly faces after a trying journey.

The train from Edinburgh was full to bursting point and most of the soldiers on board were returning to France and had prepared for their journey in true Scotch style. We lost two of our men at once and didn't find them until we were well into England. By then they were very Scottish!

It was like being back on the ranch again trying to herd them all to Folkestone, but we did somehow and we crossed at night. Everything was blacked out, I stood on deck and all you could hear was the swoosh of water as we carved our way swiftly towards France.

We arrived in Boulogne in the early morning, but one would hardly have known one was in France. There was khaki everywhere and nothing but English voices. It took an age for us to find anyone who could tell us where we were supposed to go. It was an extremely warm day and the men were weighed down with a ton of kit.

After several wrong turnings we were at last pointed towards the station where another tightly packed train awaited. This one was in considerably worse condition than the one down from Edinburgh. It was sweltering inside. I spoke to some very glum officers from a Welsh regiment who were returning to the front. They had been wounded at Neuve Chappelle and were not in a hurry to return. I can tell you it did not do much for my state, listening to their stories in that boiler of a compartment and I was very glad when we arrived at our destination.

Before the war I imagine it was a pretty wee village, now it has been swamped by the army and is a mass of men and munitions. There our little group met up with a larger detachment bound for the battalion, including a couple of officers who were returning after being wounded. They were much brighter fellows than the Welsh. A Captain Barker was in command of the whole lot of us, now nearly 200 strong, and he led us off towards the Brigade's depot where we were to stay the night before joining the battalion the following morning.

What he did not pass on until we were on the road out of the village and past the endless rows of tents and huts was that we were to get there on foot! 15 miles under a boiling sun with all our kit. It was quite an afternoon I can tell you, altho' only four men dropped out. They made their own way to the depot some hours after the rest of us had collapsed into our tents.

The next morning there was more marching for our weary band but at last we reached the battalion. They were making ready to go up that evening and everyone was frightfully busy. Myself and the two others from the 3rd, Bill Cassidy and Tom Stephen, stood around feeling like spare parts.

When the sun started to set we went up, going into the trenches not far from where that large battle was fought. It was all rather confusing. A guide led us from a sunken road into the first of the reserve trenches and from there we zigzagged our way forward.

It took an age as there was a stream of men coming the other way. We all had our kit on and the communication trenches are narrow so it was a tight squeeze. It was pitch black and every now and then a flare would burst in the sky and suddenly you would get a glimpse of what was going on. We were lucky to go in when it was very quiet, only the flares and the odd tugga-tugga of a machine gun sounding further down the line.

The next morning felt like the first day at school. One feels a constant fluttering in the stomach at first, but slowly that recedes and one settles down to business. What needs to be done, must be done!

Us three new arrivals have all been split up and are in different companies, I haven't seen either of them since we came into the line.

I am writing again later as I had to stop all of a sudden earlier. It is now evening on the same day. It's dark and the stand-to has finished and I have a little time to finish this before doing my 'rounds'. I was interrupted earlier as the Bosche are terribly jumpy at the moment and decided to take that moment to give us a spot of hate.

Anyhow it is all quiet now and I can continue.

So it was all rather confusing at first. Everyone else knew exactly what they were doing so I just followed blithely along. To begin with my men were leading me but you do quickly pick things up. Most of them are regulars, they were in India and some had fought in South Africa too, but their ranks are thinning and being filled with the likes of myself and the draft I came out with. They are sturdy men, many from Glasgow altho' there are plenty of Highlanders too and even one or two Englishmen!

That first day was very quiet, nevertheless I had that butterfly feel in my stomach the whole time. I felt very much as if I was on trial and I was ever so anxious not to let anyone down, particularly so as everyone knows I am Charlie's brother. I do hope I will not let him down. I will try my very best.

My first job that night (it is after dark when we do most of our work) was to take a working party to try and improve the 'sanitation'. When in Scotland one pondered the death or glory that awaited in France, digging latrines did not loom large in the scheme of things!

The next day I heard my first shelling. Fortunately it was aimed behind us, tho' it is at first a thoroughly unnerving experience. The old hands are rather blasé about it all and say one soon gets used to it. It just becomes part of the routine.

The trenches are very different to how dear Charlie described them when he was out here, you see they change character with the seasons.

To begin with it was ever so dusty and one is always thirsty. Indeed thirst and fatigue are always there when you are in the line. We really get very little time to sleep and one finds oneself cat-napping at every opportunity. I do feel weary.

Between the trenches wheat sprouts in great clumps in no-man's land and the shell holes are full of grass and wild flowers. There are a surprising number of birds too. On my second afternoon (it is the afternoons when we normally have a time to sleep or write), it was surprisingly still and peaceful and we could hear birds singing happily.

It all changed three days ago when there was a terrific thunderstorm. It had been getting hotter and hotter and then it broke. It was like Rhodesia and by lunchtime we were sitting in a quagmire. Just to add to our comforts, the Bosche chose that moment to bomb us. We launched a vigorous retaliation to quieten him down. When that was all done with we were left with a colossal repair job as our trench was in an awful state and we have spent the last few days trying to put things right.

The rain has made for a pretty miserable few days and the Bosche have been busy too. They are very active and we fear an attack but don't worry about me. Once out here and settled into the battalion I feel very safe, besides being killed seems somehow a very distant possibility when you are just a tiny part of this huge military machine over here. I am not an individual, rather a small insignificant cog, oiled with mud, mud and more mud!

I must go out round the sentries now so I will end here. Please write soon and tell everyone to write. I do so long to get letters.

Mother, have you finished those socks yet? Please also will you send me several pairs of thick ones, like those I use for walking on the hill as I am going through my socks very quickly.

All my love from France,
Ronnie

★ ★ ★

Ronnie, June 19, 1915
France

Hello Little Ben,

Thank you for your letter. I do like getting letters as it really brightens one's day out here. Usually I don't open them at once but save them for a quiet moment when I can sit down and read them properly. I spend the day in anticipation of my 'treat'. And do write about what you are up to and any news at all, it is not at all strange or wrong for you to do that even if I am out here and you are 'safely back home'. Your time out here will come and then you will realise how pleasant it is to hear all the happenings from back home.

A motorcycle sounds a very good idea but I would have to try one before saying yes. I might prefer a horse. Anyhow what choice do I have – you outrank me!

I have learned nothing new about Charlie's fate and I don't think I'm likely to discover anything out here before it reaches back home. I think Dad will be the first to hear, but dear Ted do not raise your hopes. One of the officers from Charlie's company told me that it was a terribly fierce set-to and he doesn't hold out much hope he would have come through. The Germans and Red Cross are also usually pretty quick to pass on details of those captured. It is best we face it.

You wanted to know what would be useful to add to your kit. The great thing is to keep it small and water tight. Too many arrive as if they are out for a big game shoot. They are not unlike some of the Americans one used to meet in Rhodesia! (I believe I did tell you of them in a letter once? – my, do those days seem an age ago!)

The most important thing above all is socks and plenty of them. Mother has just sent me out a bundle of thick socks I used when walking up north and they are proving fine. I am sure it will be entirely different come winter, but for the moment make sure your boots are in top condition and you have a waterproof of some sort, a cape perhaps would be a good idea for the summer as it has been too warm for a coat. Handkerchiefs are always useful and the air cushion I brought out has proved as invaluable as Charlie said it would. Whatever you decide you mustn't overload yourself.

You need not bring a year's supply of candles or soap – it is not as if, despite beliefs to the contrary, the French live in the dark and refuse to wash! Not that we have much opportunity for a good wash ourselves when we are in the line, mind that should suit you wee Ben!!

Envelopes and writing paper are much in demand so I would bring plenty. I include a more comprehensive list that we worked out between three of us officers and our servant in our dugout during a quiet time the other afternoon. All the others have been out considerably longer than I have so list with some authority. I must stress you really do not want to be overburdened.

We have been in the line now for around two weeks and I am extremely tired. It is much longer than a normal tour and we have no idea why we are being kept in for so long. The weather has at least improved but the Bosche opposite have been jolly jumpy throughout and our front trench is constantly being bombed. They have all sorts of frightful devices they try to get at us with. First there is the usual shelling but often that is aimed behind us at the support line or further to the rear. Our main concern is the 'whizz-bangs'. They are brutes. With the shelling there is time to find a spot of cover, as they generally whistle as if in warning, and stay there till it's over but the whizz-bangs arrive unannounced. They have a flat trajectory and hurry over, usually in salvoes of four along your line. They can give one quite a shock.

There are also bombs and rifle grenades. In the night, altho' sometimes in the day as well, a Bosche patrol will try and sneak over no-man's land and then hurl bombs into our trench. This will be followed by a burst of 'whizz-bangs' or rifle grenades and for an hour or so all hell will break loose. It is usual for us to send a counter patrol out straight away to bomb them back and they usually respond by calling on their guns and we'll do likewise and it will continue like that for a while before everyone has had enough and retires to bed to snatch an hour's sleep before stand to.

I haven't been over the top yet. I am considered still too much the novice for anything like that, but they say it is a most exhilarating experience. I am also still to fire a shot at the Bosche!

Most nights I have to tour all our sentries. I go with Sergeant Morton, who has been out here since the battalion arrived in France in November (he knew Charlie). He has been a great help in showing me what to do and what to look out for. I showed him your list and he thought it fine.

He's a real blessing at night as it is easy to get lost or spooked when on your own. He is always telling stories. Last night he told a tale he'd heard from a sergeant in the battalion we replaced in the line (a tremendous amount of gossiping goes on – worse than a line of Glasgow women at the butchers!). They had been in a different part of the front, further south than we are now. This sergeant was doing the rounds with an officer and discovered one of their sentries was missing. There was not a sign of him. Later that night another one disappeared without a sound and the next night another. This caused much disquiet amongst the men, they swore blind they had no idea where they had got to nor had they seen nor heard a squeak.

The next night they found out what had happened when they caught the Bosche in the act. They would select two of their biggest men, arm them with truncheons and send them out with a patrol who would sneak up to our trench. Then one of the gorillas would bop the unsuspecting sentry with his truncheon, they'd lean over and catch him before he fell and lift him out of the trench and carry the poor unconscious chap back to their line. All done with little fuss and next to no noise.

True or not, it has put the fear of God into our wretched sentries. It has actually made them rather jumpy and they are liable to loose off a couple of rounds in our direction unless we identify ourselves in good time. I suggested to the sergeant he might be a little more cautious with his stories in future!

Must call a halt now as I have the chance to sleep for an hour or two. Really Ted it is the tiredness that weighs on one the most out here. That apart and a spot of mud and the odd hate, life is not so bad, but I do look forward to getting out and having a rest.

love,
Ronnie

★ ★ ★

Kit list for Teddie
One cap
Three pairs of breeches or trousers
A pair of shorts (depending when you come out)
Two pairs of boots
At least six pair of socks

10 handkerchiefs (not white)
Four flannel shirts
Four thick vests
Five pairs of long woolly draws
A woolly
One comforter
One wool sleeping cap
A warm British coat and a macintosh or waterproof cape
Pipe and tobacco or cigarettes (bring plenty)
Two woollen scarves
A pair of gloves (not woollen)
A flask (and a bottle of brandy to fill it with, a nip helps one through the night and settles the nerves!)
One waterproof carrier
One waterproof sheet
One revolver (for dealing with the Hun!)

* * *

Ronnie, June 24, 1915
France

Dearest Bertie,

Out at last! We have finally been relieved and our [sic] now back in billets at La G_____. What a relief.

We were in the line for 16 days, which is the longest the battalion has spent in the trenches since it arrived in France. Every man from the Colonel down to the youngest ranker was utterly exhausted by the time we got back here. The relief seemed to take an eternity. We were fortunate that our final couple of days were quiet and the Bosche kept quiet as we were leaving. It has dried out too which helped enormously but the numbers of burdened men wedged into the slender communication lines made it all frustratingly slow.

We were all filthy dirty! – you cannot imagine, so covered in dried mud I believe our clothes would have stood of their own accord. Stepping into a hot bath when we reached our billets is an experience I do not believe I will ever better!

We have been back here for three days now. We had the first one to clean and rest but the Army are loath to leave you idle and it has had us all training like mad for the last couple of days. Tomorrow we are to route march, a treat that has met with little appreciation at any level in my company. The day after that is to be a day for sports and we are to have aquatic sports in the canal as well.

In Rhodesia I was told never to set foot in water as all manner of dangers lurked and having looked at the canal here it is an advice I intend to bide by!

Still it is a relief to be out for a time. It gives a moment to consider my baptism as a soldier. I did promise to be honest and open with you and I have been and will continue to be. It is for you to decide whether to pass that on and to whom.

I can say that after the initial apprehension I was largely not afraid. One becomes rather accepting of one's lot. Us Britons are a stoical lot. I think my only fear is of being maimed or disabled for life. The talk among the men is of catching a 'Blighty' but if that means a life without a limb or your abilities I would rather catch it all.

Shelling is the other thing that stretches the nerves but much of it all comes, I believe, from the fatigue. Sometimes one's mind is fuddled by a lack of sleep and one can't quite put things in the right order.

When it rained it was miserable and the dugouts are not much comfort, unless the Bosche are chucking things at you! Yet the men are magnificent and there is a tremendous regard for each other. Some fellows who one would not come across at all in civilian life, or indeed care for, are the stoutest around.

Tom Stephens and Bill Cassidy both came through. I spoke with them over a bottle of vin blanc (at the cost of a franc there are compensations for being out here!) and they feel much the same as I. We wouldn't miss it for the world despite all the horridness.

I saw Frank Donald yesterday. His uniform makes him look even smaller! He was in fine spirits and will write to you soon with all his news. Like all of us out here he is always keen to receive letters so do put pen to paper Bertie.

Yesterday I had time with Captain Inglis to talk about Charlie. I thought I might be able to talk to people out here but he said all that had been done and, difficult as it is, we can only wait. He said if Charlie was a prisoner we should have heard some news by now, altho' if he had been badly wounded he may not be in a condition to pass on any news. Do you think of him much?

Do write soon Bertie and tell me what you think of what I have said. Please send my love to Gertrude and my nephews. Tell me news of Allan too.

All my love,
Ronnie

★ ★ ★

Diary of Nora Anderson, July 4, 1915
Strathairly

Willie has decided that all letters and telegrams should be sent here as I will always be here to receive them. If they went to Glasgow he may have already left for work or have not been at home on account of his Red Cross business and then we would not know.

After breakfast I sit and wait. I listen for the sound of the postman's bicycle as it comes up the lane. I cannot do anything else, only wait. I have tried to write then, as it is a quiet moment, but if I write I cannot listen.

There is still no other news.

★ ★ ★

Teddie, July 12, 1915
Dunfermline

Dear Ron,

I hope this finds you well in France. Life is a terrible bore here in Fifeshire. I have marched more men up more hills than the old Duke of York did.

I am going to try for the Royal Flying Corps. I think that will be the quickest way out to France. They want pilots and I would like to try my hand at it. They say that if you can handle a motorcycle or are good on a horse then you will be suited to flying. Maybe you should try it as well. Have you seen much of them in France? At Montrose they told me the training lasts a few months and then once you have passed the examinations it will be straight over to France.

I hope you have had a chance to sleep a bit. Perhaps it's doing you good. Mother always said you slept too much!

If you write to me don't hide things from me. I know you tell all to Bertie so I should know too. I will be coming out as well. I am not a boy anymore.

Thank you for the list. It has caused much discussion in the mess. Have you fired at the Hun yet?

The weekend before last I went over to Woodbank as Bertie, Gertrude and the boys were all there. Tuppie was there as well. She was asking me about Charlie so I told her what you had said. She looked very sad. Allan Gilmour came for Sunday. He is being moved down to England and thinks that means they will be off to France soon enough. He said he means to write to you soon.

I have been playing golf once a week and am getting much better now. It does not make us very popular as people think we shouldn't play during the war. They also see us in no uniforms and think we are not doing our duty. On one occasion we were even handed one of the dreaded goose feathers so now we play in uniform!

I saw in the paper that Brodie Galbraith has been killed in the Dardanelles. All his brothers are serving as well.

Do you get to have a look at the papers at all or would you like me to write and tell you things from them?

I will write again when I have news. Please tell me if you think I should try for the RFC.

love,

Teddie

★ ★ ★

Ronnie, July 17, 1915

France

Dear Mother & Dad,

We are back in billets again and I am sitting in a chair with my jacket off enjoying the sunshine. We came out the night before last but did not reach our billets until three o'clock in the morning. After we had left the line we had to march all the way here with all our kit. Everyone was ready to drop by the time we arrived. We are in tents but with the weather fine it is really very pleasant and the war seems quite distant at present.

It was a blessed relief to take one's clothes off after 17 days. Last night I actually wore pyjamas!

Thank you for all your letters and the parcel, but I need to tell you some things about parcels. They get a terrible battering on the way out and unfortunately the one you sent failed to pull through! It is best not to send things that can't survive a bit of a set to. There wasn't much of the cake left I'm afraid. Cheese in a sturdy box is a good thing to send and chocolate is always popular and it doesn't matter much if that gets thrown around. It is good to get newspapers as well. Let's us know how we're getting on!

Our company mess has a policy for parcels. We take out any personal bits and pieces and then put them all together so we can all share in someone's good fortune. We have had some feasts in the trenches, well they seem like feasts at the time. The rations we get given are horrid, our mess servant tries nobly to make them into something edible but the poor chap has not had much success.

This last turn was quite different from my first. It was much drier and sunny nearly the whole time. On the down side that made it very hot and water is in quite short supply so one's tongue is just about hanging out the whole time. Overall it was a pretty quiet time, altho' there was one to-do I will tell you about.

On the first night I went out on my first patrol which to begin with was nerve-wracking indeed. Once you are up and over the parapet and out into the darkness of no-man's land you soon calm yourself.

I had my old friend Sergeant Morton with me which was a great comfort as he knew his way around, which is jolly difficult in the pitch black and muddle of no-man's land – all shell holes look alike to me! So we scurried about in the dark for a time before returning unseen to our own lines.

There had not been much to see and the Bosche were being very quiet so there was not much to put in the report. It was still a relief to get back and altho' I felt quite normal when I went to light a cigarette I noticed my hand was shaking. Thankfully no-one else appeared to notice, or if they did I think it is pretty well accepted that one's body may react peculiarly every now and then to all the oddities out here. I'm sure it makes for an interesting study for all the doctors and so forth.

Anyhow, none of our patrols found much to report that night and so the next few days were more-or-less peaceful.

We were busy at night working on the wire and repairing the trenches. At first the CO wanted our machine guns to keep unleashing odd bursts on the Bosche but that led to them replying which stopped us wiring so we stopped firing and they did too and then we could get on with our wiring! It is a thankless task but without any interruptions it at least meant we could get it done as quickly as possible.

During the days we were left pretty much to ourselves altho' them opposite insisted on shelling us at intervals which prevented us catching up on much sleep. I am still finding the fatigue the hardest thing out here.

Anyhow that to-do I mentioned, it begun in the middle of the night of the 9th. We were told that the Bosche were massing in their trenches and we had to stand to. We stood ready until after dawn, expecting an attack but it stayed quiet and there were even fewer flares than normal. The following day passed as normal, we were shelled again, which I am used to now. That apart it was again quiet.

That night the same thing happened, we had to rush from our dug-out and rouse the men to fix bayonets and stand by for an attack. The long night was spent again without incident, tho' with no less anxiety. So the next night we sent out a patrol and they found the Bosche wire had been cut. Now that is another sign an attack is on the way so we stood to throughout the night – a third night in a row with no sleep. We kept firing rapid bursts at the hole in the wire until the neighbouring battalion requested us to stop as they were being shelled in retaliation.

The next day, the 12th, we could hear the Bosche working in their trenches which further convinced our CO an attack was on the way. By now everyone was jumpy as we had not had a deal of sleep. There was a lot of sniping going on as well. That is very trying as I have to be ever so careful about where I am as the depth of the trenches can vary from place to place and I seem to be taller than most out here. I spend much of the time walking hunched over – if the war lasts I shall return home bent in two! It is a war for the pygmy!!

For the next two tiresome nights we were stood to again and on the day we were relieved there were suspicions the Bosche might be about to use gas as we saw some pipes being set up above their parapet. That meant for an uneasy time and were very glad to come out.

The battalion put a cross up during that last stay in memory of the eight officers and 106 men we lost at Neuve Chappelle. They did the same at the place where Charlie and all those others went over and I shall see it if we go into the line there. There is a chance of that as it is in this area. Won't that be strange.

Thank you again for all the letters from you both. Teddie and Bertie are very good too and I have had a letter from Allan Gilmour as well.

How is everything at home? Strathairly is wonderful at this time of the year I always think. Even Glasgow loses some of its greyness in July. I wonder where I shall go when this is over?

Your ever loving son,
Ronnie

★ ★ ★

August 12, 1915
The Times, London

Lt CH Anderson, 1st HLI, who was reported missing on December 19, 1914, is now stated to have been killed in action near Givenchy on that date. He was the third son of Mr William J Anderson, Glasgow, and was educated at Cargilfield, Fettes College and Sandhurst. He was gazetted Second Lieutenant in October 1908, and Lieutenant in 1911.

CHAPTER 6

DEPARTURES

Ronnie, August 17, 1915
France

Dearest Mother,

I do not need a candle to write to you tonight. I now write my letters at night, once things have settled down and the men have been dispatched for their chores. Chores!! What chores!

Tonight is particularly quiet, one might even say peaceful. I'm on duty but I have half an hour or so before the sergeant comes to collect me and we go off on our rounds. In this sector it is not an onerous task at present – they seem a docile lot opposite, Saxons I think – and the sentries are so pleased to see you for a few moments, just to exchange a word or two to break the monotonous fear of being out there in the dark on their own.

Much of life here is monotonous, stilted fear you know. We wait yards apart for hundreds and hundreds of miles. We wait, dig and then wait.

Wait, wait and wait.

Dig, dig and dig.

Waiting for what? There is only one thing we are waiting for out here.

Tonight the moon is full and it is making me maudlin (one battles constantly to bury one's feelings, one really can't afford to let them interfere, nothing would get done otherwise and we'd all come home). I now rather write at night because it is usually dark and one cannot see the awfulness of one's surrounds. Night is a dark veil drawn across a tortured landscape. I usually write in the depths of my dugout, hunched beside a flickering candle scribbling a page at a time for there is always something to interrupt (most people out here write in the afternoon when there are less jobs to be seen to). Tonight is different.

I have come out to the trench to pen this as it is clear almost as day because of the moon. It is a warm night and dry, which is the most important thing. I have brought a box up from the dugout on which I sit. A soldier is sleeping soundlessly a few yards from me, his hands clutching his rifle.

This night finds me in a peculiar frame. If I stood up and looked across this ghastly, ghostly illuminated land, I would see towards where Charlie went over. It is sight which one could have never imagined, desolate, featureless country. A desert. No-one could have survived going out there.

He is gone. We should never have hoped. You see, out here no-one disappears and comes back. It does not happen. He would have turned 27 in just a few hours from now.

Can you still see his face?

Poor Charlie, he always held such enthusiasm. He was such a trier, such a smiler. I loved him, my brother.

I try and wash every day, Mother, as I know you would want me to. But I wash to try and rid myself of the stench that hangs everywhere here. It is a smell you should wish never to experience, but it is one I fear I will forever sense until my dying day. When I was washing this evening in muddy water from a canteen out of which I would later eat, I thought of the marble basins, warm and peaty water, dry towels and scented soap of old Scotland; to think that a land does exist where people still bathe, where people dine at their leisure, where people still walk upright and tall. Where people are people.

If I walked in the door now I do not think you would recognise me, even if I were clean and presentable. Being out here ages you. Days are like months and weeks stretch into years. You cannot imagine the horror of it. If I get killed, Mother, don't say 'so like Ron's careless way'. I want to be remembered as Charlie is. I can still see him.

The sergeant is coming so I must go now.

With all my love,

your son,

Ronnie

* * *

50

Bertie, August 26, 1915
Gailes, Ayrshire

Dear Ron,

This is not a tone I care to take, yet I must take you to task for your last letter to Mother. Do you think you should write to her in that dreadful tone? It upsets and alarms her. Do consider what she and Dad have suffered with Charlie. They have lost a son and we have lost a brother. We have all lost.

Everyone is suffering. It is everywhere. I detest upbraiding you Ronnie and it seems as if I always am, but it was not fair of you to write like that to Mother. If you must, write like that to me. There is no way home until it is all over. We have to go on together now as if Charlie were still here. He was a soldier and so are we all now. Take heart Ron, you are not alone.

I saw this poem in the newspaper. It was written by an officer who was killed in France. Before he died he sent it to a friend after his brother had been killed, and the friend later sent it to the papers.

'O heart and soul and careless played
Our little band of brothers,
And never recked the time would come
To change our game for others.
It's joy for those who played with you
To picture now what grace
Was in your mind and single heart
And in your radiant face.
Your light-foot strength by flood and field
For England keener glowed;
To whatsoever things are fair
We know, through you, the road.
Nor is our grief the less thereby;
O swift and sting and dear, Good-bye.'

Brother, we are all grieving. You are not alone and neither are we alone in our grief. Be strong, my brother.

I have been moved here to Gailes. E company is now no longer part of the 17th but has been made into the new 19th battalion. It means we have been left behind here while the 17th have moved down to England. We are to be the regiment's reserve battalion under Bill Auld's command. Gertrude is being kept busy helping Mrs Auld run the soldiers home.

Dad is working ever so hard. The firm still has to run despite having so few people and he is always hurrying round Glasgow and beyond on Red Cross duty. They have raised an enormous sum of money already.

I have not heard from Little Ben of late. I fear he is bored to distraction in Dunfermline. The last time I saw him he was full of the RFC but whether he has pressed ahead with that I do not know.

Thomas Stout has been killed, he played rugby with Allan in Glasgow. He was with the Cameronians in the Dardanelles. The 7th HLI are out there as well and they've suffered heavy casualties. Stuart Gemmell was one of them.

I think Teddie may be destined for there at this rate. I do hope he goes ahead with his idea to try for the flyers.

We are all thinking of you and praying for you, Ronnie. Hold on dear brother.

With all my love,
Bertie

★ ★ ★

Diary of Nora Anderson, September 7, 1915
Strathairly

Willie assured me yesterday that telegrams will now certainly come here. He has corrected the mistake at the Post Office. He still looks grey. I think he has aged. I wonder if I have? It must be likely. At least we know now. Although as yet I feel no better for knowing and I strongly believed that I would.

I have taken time to write properly again. There have been many days over this summer when I did not even want to glimpse the dark red cover of my journal, let alone unclasp it and turn to the first empty page. There were days when catching sight of it as I opened my dressing table drawer made me shrink as if from life itself. Sometimes I just sit on my stool and stare into the mirror, seeing nothing and thinking nothing, or rather nothing that I can now recall.

Now I want to write my dear journal again. Jean was right. I have missed it and believe also that it does help me in some small way in these dark days. No-one knows of it – it is my secret. Perhaps one day, when I am gone, others shall see it and I do not think I should mind that anymore.

Norman told me that it took an age to find Willie. They should never have sent the telegram to the office. Norman said that as soon as Willie walked through the door and saw everyone turn to him that he knew. He went straight to his office and closed the door.

Willie has said little to me. I spoke with Jean. She kindly came to visit last weekend after she heard the news. She said I must let Willie be. They say for a father to lose a son is torture on earth. They do not say what it is for a mother. Do they even wonder?

I am not told many of the details of the horrors that our young men are encountering. They regard it as a cruelty to tell a mother such things. I believe Bertie tells me the truth, yet he does not want others to.

I have not shown Ronnie's last letter to Willie. I have not replied to it either. I do not think I can. I spoke to Bertie of it and he was furious. I asked him to not tell anybody about it, especially his father. Ronnie has always been different and I think we should make allowances for him at a time like this. I don't want to think of it any further.

Bertie has done wonders, and Teddie too wrote me a wonderful letter. Bertie says we will have a service for Him when this is all over and I would so like that, just a small family gathering to send him away properly once and for all. It would be a good thing to do for us all and for Him. I wonder where Willie would want it to be?

McCullum told me that Mr Todd had cut His name out of the list for his window as he knows I do not care for the practice.

I should write to Ronnie. I wonder what Willie has said. We have not spoken of Him. I do not suppose we shall until this is all done with. It will not bring Him back.

★ ★ ★

Ronnie, September 27, 1915
France

Dear Bertie,

We're going back into the line again tomorrow which comes almost as a blessed relief after the week or so that has just passed. I am sure you have seen in the newspapers of the great attack at Loos. The last time I wrote to you we were in the midst of preparing for just that but I could not breathe a word of it to a single soul (even you my dear, wise older brother!). We haven't actually been in the front line for more than a month. We had a turn in brigade reserve and then it was off behind the lines where the front was only a distant rumble.

For three weeks we were working like dervishes practising for the big day. They had made a giant model of the land over which we were to advance and we would spend long spells standing on this platform that overlooked the panorama, studying it and committing it deep to memory.

One day we were marched off early in the morning all spruced up to the wee town of L'E_____ where we were inspected by Lord Kitchener himself. After giving us a good look over he sat on his horse and spoke to us. He complimented our appearance and also remarked that our sterling work in the line deserved praise. Then we marched all the way back to our billets and got on with training!

We were to be one of the support waves and on the 24th we were marched up to corps reserve where we spent an uncomfortable night out in a sorry scrape of a trench. There were thousands upon thousands of troops, the ground was covered in a gigantic khaki blanket. And we sat there more or less in the open whilst a great barrage begun to pound the Bosche. Few were able to sleep, for most of us this was to be our first time over the top and it was an uneasy time.

We waited through the night and at shortly after five, just before dawn began to break, we were stood to. It was then I suppose that I felt what can only have been real fear – whatever it was it was most certainly a new feeling for me. It is an odd thing. It strikes at a time of inactivity, when one is waiting and all one can think about is the job at hand. The only parallel I can draw (and it is a hopelessly inadequate one as I have never been very good at this sort of thing) is when waiting for the off of some sporting occasion. Your stomach is twitching and turning, your palms clammy and your hand is not entirely still, but once the whistle blows it's the game and only the game. Sounds silly I know, but magnify that by the largest number you can think of and that's what it is like. Not pleasant, but one bares it and it is soon over. I suppose the next time will be much simpler.

Amid all this there was one amazing sight. There is this enormous iron structure, once part of a factory I would have thought, that bestrides the skyline at Loos, it's had a bit of a battering and is rather skeletal. It is known as Tower Bridge and as we were waiting, each man lost within himself, a wonderful double rainbow appeared over it. It was a comforting distraction as we waited, ready for the command at any moment, for three interminable hours.

There had been a dreadful mix up with our gas and it was all rather confusing, but in the end the whistles finally went and we advanced. There was really no time to think about anything but encouraging the men and keeping everyone going forward. Occasionally one was aware of the whistle of a bullet or a gap appearing in the ranks but now, trying to think about it carefully, I remember little real detail. I am not even altogether sure how long it all lasted and all of a sudden it was over and we were withdrawn back to the Rue du P_____ without really having got involved. I have still to loose off a shot in anger.

Those ahead had suffered terribly we heard and they had been forced to call off the attack. I am afraid to say there will be some long lists in the newspapers in the next few days. I hear that Norman MacLeod was wounded and his battalion suffered most heavily.

I have had to write letters to the families of two men who were killed in my platoon. That is a frightful task I can tell you.

So now it is back to the old routine. We have been lucky in a way to be involved with the attack as it meant all that time behind the lines as well as good food and some time for rest and I think we all needed it after long spells in the line which really leave one exhausted. We had porridge for most breakfasts and also eggs and bacon. They like to fatten you up before an attack!

They also laid on a regatta day at the Indian Ammunition Park. That was an extraordinary day. The weather has been pretty miserable. We were billeted alongside a road that was a constant haze of red dust that got everywhere such was the weight of men, wagons and motors plying back and forth. Then we woke up one morning and the dust was gone. Joy! But no. It had rained and the whole thing had become a black sea of mud. So a regatta day was a safe enough fixture as the rain could not ruin that.

We had swimming and diving events but also some splendid ones like jousting. It made for jolly viewing. They made rafts by lashing together empty petrol tanks and covering them with boards. One man rowed while the other stood armed with a mop and attempted to dislodge their opponent. A great crowd of locals turned out to watch as well as the usual mass of soldiers.

The weather is really turning now and there is just mud everywhere. The trenches are all a bit of a mess and the odour is none too savoury either. We have had the unpleasant experience of turning up long dead men as we attempt to affect repairs by digging ever deeper.

Thank you for sending the bundle of books. What a good idea to print them like that. They have all been seized upon and everyone is devouring them.

Colonel Hill has gone up to take command of brigade so we will get a new CO. He is from the Connaught Rangers and arrives tomorrow in time to take us up to the line.

Did you see David Galbraith has been killed?

I am sure the budget will be keeping Dad busy and no doubt you have poured over it. Reading about taxes rising and falling in a trench is most peculiar!

You must not worry about me, you really must not – I am in the pink right now. Absolutely in the pink, dear brother. I hope you can be proud of me once more. My moment is done and gone.

With love,

Ronnie

★ ★ ★

Ronnie, October 4, 1915
France

My dear Mother and Dad,

La Melasse, La Gadoue, La Mouscaille. They are all words to describe mud. See I have not been wasting my time out here; I am learning a new language. It is like we are a different race, blackened from head to foot. It gets everywhere, we even exist on a diet of mud. Mud porridge, bacon and mud, biscuits spread with good thick French mud and, finally, mud pudding and a drop of port.

I could write a paper on mud. It comes in all different matters, sometimes thick, sometimes thin, sometimes thick and thin. At some point one is bound to fall in and it is just a question of luck as to how deep your particular hole is, whether it's up to your knees, your waist or, God forbid, neck. If you don't fall in, the duckboards that once covered the floor of the trench but now exist below the surface sludge sometimes give you a helping hand. If you are unfortunate enough to stand on the end of one it can spring up and strike you a healthy blow, rather like a man stepping on a rake. Oh the perils of trench life! Yet hardly anyone grumbles, we all just plod onwards. Resigned to our muddy lot I suppose.

We came back into the line yesterday and have so far been blessed with peace and quiet. This particular little stretch has a reputation of being restful and so far it is been just that. Long may it continue we all say.

Thank you for the gruyere. It was very well received in the mess and I still have some to help me through this little stint. You did terribly well to think I might like it.

I have just finished my first round and write this whilst I wait to go out again as there is little point in trying to sleep for such a short time, it would just make me ratty. It is odd, when it is most peaceful one tends to go round more often as the quiet can be strangely unnerving, one becomes convinced they are up to something.

Tonight is one of those that has almost a peculiar beauty to it. Further up the line there is obviously some activity as the sky is alive. The flares create happy patterns in the sky and like a child watching on Guy Fawkes night one can't but help smiling at the bright colours. Little things! It was always so with me, was it not Dad?!

I must tell you this story of my command of French. You must pass this on to Bertie as well. He's not the only linguist in the family now!

After our last spell in the line we were relieved and marched some way back out of harm's way. There the battalion were all given baths and allowed to have the remainder of the day at their leisure. I decided to take a walk through the small town where we were. I was passing an 'estaminet', they are little cafes or bars where the troops go to drink cheap 'vin blanc', when I heard a commotion. I stepped inside and there were three Glasgow men from the battalion having a furious set to with the chubby little French proprietor. I stepped in and with my finest French brought about a compromise that was accepted on both sides and off went Glasgow's finest. The French proprietor turned to his white knight (that is moi by the way, in case you are wondering) and said 'je comprends bien Les Anglais et je comprends les soldats a Irelande (at this point he throws up his hands) mais je ne comprends pas Les Ecossais'. Whereupon he pushed a bottle of the evil liquid into my hand and ushered me back into the street.

So on we go. I think the winter will be a pretty miserable experience, but at least one is surrounded by the best of fellows.

Do send more of that gruyere, that would certainly help the winter pass by!

I hope you are both well and I am sure fortune will now have in its turn to favour us. I will be a son to make you both proud.

Your loving son,

Ron

★ ★ ★

War diary, 1st Battalion, Highland Light Infantry, October 8, 1915

A quiet day. A hostile patrol was located on one front about 11.30pm. Second Lieutenant AR Anderson killed.

★ ★ ★

Diary of Nora Anderson, October 12, 1915
Glasgow

This is the first night I have spent back here for such a long time. The house is so cold. Willie uses it for sleep and that is all. I don't think there is often a fire on in the drawing room anymore. He works all hours now. Hour after hour. Some weekends he does not come to Strathairly. Instead he volunteers to make Red Cross trips to Perth or Dumfries, to Dundee or Berwick. It is always work. I see very little of him, but then that is now. He must do what is required of him.

He was waiting when I arrived from the station. I showed him the telegram. He read it and folded it very neatly, once, twice, and put it in his jacket pocket. Then we sat down.

He took a paper from his other pocket it and opened it up. It was a letter from the company commander. I can't remember his name now. I am trying hard to think of it as I would like to write it down. Willie has the letter and I must ask him in the morning for the captain's name.

Willie says the announcement will be in tomorrow's casualty lists. I wonder if Mr Todd will remove it. We tried to think of anybody we should contact so that they do not have to learn the news in that dreadful manner. Can you imagine opening your newspaper and spying a name that meant so much to you? I sent word to his brothers this morning. It was by telegram as I could not think how else would be better. I found it difficult to think properly. I felt ever so tired, actually weary everywhere. Especially in my head.

Yet now I do not want to sleep. I still feel tired, but I do not want to walk to the bed and lie down.

Willie read the letter to me and then folded it up again and returned it to his pocket. He did not show it to me. In the morning I shall ask for it and read it again in my own time.

It happened at a place called Rue de Bois. I should imagine that before the war it was rather a lovely place. The captain said that it was quick and he would not have felt anything. This I do remember very definitely. The captain wrote that he 'looked at peace and had not a blemish on his handsome face. He was a happy fellow and brought much joy to all who served with him'.

It is so like him, to forget to duck. He was always forgetting things, a day dreamer, always able to forget where he was and imagine himself somewhere so much better. Perhaps he is now.

The captain also informed us where he has been laid to rest. He said that they were able to have a wee ceremony with his servant, the captain and two other officers as the part of the line they are manning is so quiet at the moment.

I was knitting him another pair of socks to go in his next parcel. Willie was hopeful of getting some of that gruyere cheese he has come to like so much. I find it calming to pack his parcels. I imagine him opening them at the front. The delight on his face. He was like Charlie, always ready to smile, although sometimes I felt it was his only defence, an attempt to mask what lay beneath. As a child he would drop something or break something or get caught in the midst of some mischief and that smile would spread across his face. (Or perhaps Charlie had it from Ron, saw how his older brother behaved and thought that was the best way – I wonder?) One could never scold him for long. Ronnie, Ronnie, Ronnie. A smile is no defence in this life.

I will go back to Strathairly tomorrow. Willie will not mind, I'm sure. I feel safer there.

★ ★ ★

October 13, 1915
The Times, London

Fallen Officers

The death of a number of officers, whose names have not up to the present appeared in the official casualty lists, is announced in our obituary columns today.

   SECOND LIEUTENANT ALEXANDER RONALD ANDERSON, 1st HLI who was killed in France on October 8, was the second son of Mr and Mrs Wm J Anderson of 18, Woodside-terrace, Glasgow. He was born in February 1883, educated at St Salvador's School, St Andrews and Fettes College, and had since been farming in Rhodesia. He was at home when war was declared and in August 1914 enlisted in Lovat's Scouts. In March he received a commission in the 3rd HLI, and in May he was transferred to the 1st Battalion, which he joined in France the same month, His younger brother, Lt Charles Hamilton Anderson of the same regiment, was killed in December last.

CHAPTER 7

EXISTENCE

Diary of Nora Anderson, November 6, 1915
Strathairly

Willie returns tomorrow in time for lunch. I have not seen him for nearly two weeks. I hope he will stay a while as I have been missing him here.

It's become cold again this week which I hope will help me to sleep again. I spend an age each night at my journal but there never seems much on the page the following morning. I never read what I have written. Why should I? It is mine. I can do as I desire with it.

When I write it is for that moment and for what I might be troubled by in that moment. Perhaps I shall read it all in years to come as an old, old woman. Though why would I desire to be reminded of all this?

Willie has been terribly busy. I worry for him motoring in the dark to these meetings. I wish he would have somebody with him all the time, a younger man perhaps who could do the motoring, but then I don't suppose there are many spare young men anymore. Perhaps we could write and ask for Bertie to do it as it is war work after all. We could say that he is a father and it should be those without children who go out first.

It is a mother's idea though. Bertie would not do it and Willie would not let him. Perhaps I should ask McCullum to do it, though Willie would not stand for that either.

Lily's nephew has been killed. I never met him. She says he was only 19 and had never been out of Fife before he went to France. His mother received a kindly letter from his officer and a parcel with his belongings.

Willie received our parcel yesterday, he said the clothes are muddy and dear Ron kept all our letters. They have all come back. Willie will bring the letters when he comes tomorrow, but not the uniform. He wants to burn it. I asked him not to. I think we should clean it and keep it forever. It is not the uniform he was wearing on the day. That is the one they buried him in.

This morning was bright and clear and I walked with Lad down towards the firth. Lily offered to send McCullum with me, but I said no. There were still elements of the morning mist speckled across the lowest points of the fields. Lad ran ahead pausing every now and then to explore. It was cold if I stopped but if I kept moving then I felt warm enough. I walked and walked. Willie would be furious if he knew how far I went. I walked until I could see the waters of the Forth sparkling in the sunlight. It is a sight that never fails to touch me. I stood and stood watching the sparkling until I did not want to see anymore and then turned and began to retrace my steps. I found the uphill part tiring and so had to stop and rest at intervals and then at the top of the hill I turned back to look at the waters one more time. They looked as though they might be dancing and not even the dark, ugly shape of a large ship heading towards Leith could take away the brightness.

It was a day that Scotland does like no other land. My country is a land of much beauty. A wonderful creation. The Lord does work in mysterious ways.

My faith must remain strong and true. Can I find true consolation in my faith? I will have to be strong to do so and sometimes I do not feel very strong. Sometimes I feel very tired.

I wish I might have brought Gertie this way. It was unfortunate that the weather was so miserable whilst she was staying. The boys brought some joyous life to the house for three days. They have such energetic bodies, always tottering somewhere, creating miniature havoc and squealing with delight. Lily tutted and cleaned up after them but I am sure she was delighted to have them here. I do believe it brought us all alive for a time. Although I worry for Gertie. I think there are times when she finds the children a bind. I do not know how she would cope if Bertie were to go to France. We must be thankful that he will not be for some while yet, with God's help.

We did not talk about much apart from the children and her plan to move to Woodbank to be with her mother and father. Allan took ill in Gallipoli. She worries about them being on their own and worrying about their son. She also wants to be near Tuppie, who is very withdrawn says Gertie. She says that Allan will recover, but that will take time and he will be out of danger while he does. I think he is in Egypt now. I wonder if I should have asked her to stay at Strathairly for a time?

She asked of me. I told her I was well. We did not dwell on it. What purpose can it serve?

It is quiet again now they have gone. I hope to keep Willie here for a time and ensure he rests. It would be good for us to rest here together for a few days. I do feel so tired.

★ ★ ★

Bertie, November 13, 1915
Ripon

My darling,

My promotion will come through any day now. I am now to be gazetted temporary Major and will be second in command. We are well billeted here in the South Camp, not as pleasant as dear old Troon but comfortable enough. The camp here is huge and there are men everywhere. It is a scenic area roundabout and I will hopefully have the time to explore it.

Dad had another letter from one of Ronnie's friends in the 1st battalion. It seems they are destined for Gallipoli. I feel sure that is where I will end up. The losses are great there and my time must be coming.

It is only right that I do go, indeed I must go now, but I wish it would be for France as I do not want to be so far from you and the boys. At the moment Yorkshire seems far enough.

Thank you for your long letter, it was of great comfort, yet it is a feeling I cannot divorce myself from. I should not have written to him like that. How could I judge him when I have no idea of what he went through out there? I only hope I can find out by playing my part to the full.

Ronnie's friend wrote to Dad of his burial. I have copied a part of the description. It is of some comfort that at least he had a farewell.

"We carried him to a small wood in a hollow just behind the line where the battalion had begun its cemetery and there we laid a dear son, brother and friend to rest. There were four of us in attendance as well as the chaplain and he spoke a few simple words, saying he has gone on to a better place and we said a prayer for him and all his family who have suffered this loss as we passed him into God's hands. His servant, Private McGlashan, had organised the men of his platoon to make a simple wooden cross which we placed at the head of his grave. On it was written: 'Here lies 2nd Lt AR Anderson, died October 8, 1915. His soul marches on.' We would liked to have had a piper play, but that would have attracted too much unwanted attention, so instead we whistled Flowers of the Forest and then had a minute's silence. The sun was setting and there was a stillness along our part of the line as we bade our brother goodbye. He was a good man."

It seems every day in the newspaper I see a map of that area and names that are now all too recognisable. I knew some from my time over there, but I knew them as a pleasant wee town, or the place one changed trains on the way to somewhere, or the ideal venue for a spot to lunch while motoring to the south. Now they are places that will never be forgotten.

Every day I see Givenchy printed boldly across the lines and contours and everyday I think of them. The names leap from the page, all full of meaning to every household in the land, and to ours it is a meaning full of sorrow and full of desperate memories.

The mind plays tricks. I cannot absolutely remember the last time I saw either of them. I know where. It was Strathairly. I remember the lawn and it is always summer, the boys tottering over the soft green grass and Ronnie, giant Ronnie striding towards them. What trench could be deep enough for that gentle giant, deep enough to guard him from the sniper's murderous intent.

Yet onwards we march. We must for there is no other route.

There is plenty to keep me busy here. We are always getting new men – Glasgow must be close to empty – and they have to be trained and brought together. We have a good lot, keen and always ready to learn. The endless route marches are a bit of a bore but the men must be toughened up. I try and do as many as I can as I must be toughened up too!

I do not think I will be home for Christmas, so few of the men will get the opportunity I do not think it would be right for me to do so even were I to have the chance. At least at Woodbank you will have family and it can be a bright affair. It was better news to hear that Allan will make a full recovery. That must settle Meg tremendously. These dark days will not last forever – they cannot, humanity will not allow it – and then I will be home.

Thank your father for the photographs of the boys. My how they grow.

With all my love,

B

★ ★ ★

Teddie, December 18, 1915
Curragh, Ireland

Dearest Mother and Dad,

I have done it – I have flown an aeroplane!! What an experience! I tell you there is nothing quite like it. I shall live for the air from now on! It is impossible to imagine the feeling of lifting a machine off the ground and soaring upwards into the sky. I haven't done a landing yet but that will come shortly. First I have to get more time at the controls – they don't like to let us novices loose on something so valuable quite yet! They do hurry us along and I will fly my first time solo very soon I would have thought.

I will not be in Ireland all that long. The CO told us we are getting on well and it is likely we will be packed off to reserve squadrons pretty soon after we've gone solo and passed all our examinations and tests. If we pass it all we get our RFC badge and an Aero Club certificate. We do spend a deal of time sitting in classrooms being lectured to which is rather tiresome as we'd all much prefer to be up there, but I suppose it is important.

We have to learn all about the engine – we will be as knowledgeable as mechanics by the time it is all over. We also do navigation and all sorts of scientific learning as well as signalling, rigging (that's learning how the machine is kept together and how to mend the wires that crisscross between the upper and lower wings if any is broken – a skill I never thought I'd learn!).

On a normal day we have to be up before six and head off for an early bit of flying. At the moment I have an instructor in the machine with me and once we are up I take over the controls and he sets me various tasks to do, but there is still plenty of time to look around. We

65

are higher than the birds and when it is clear we can see everything. Sometimes we fly over Dublin and get a splendid view of the city – you can see all the streets and the plan of the city. We also fly out over the sea looking for boats. At the moment it is very cold up there. The weather has been horrid – some days we have not been able to get up at all and have to spend the entire time sitting in the classroom.

When you go up you put on every piece of clothing you have as well as hat, gloves, scarf but even so when you come down you are in desperate need of a hot bath and a good breakfast.

For the rest of the morning it is class. We are being taught how to link up with the infantry. What we'll have to do is go out and find them when we make an attack and then report their whereabouts back to command. We are also learning how to work with the artillery. You have to fly out over the Hun line and look for targets and when you find one you fly back to our batteries and drop them a message with the whereabouts of the Hun and then fly back to see what happens. It all sounds so interesting and it is very valuable for the Army.

We are also taught how to use the Lewis gun in case one encounters the Hun in the air and we have to know how it works too. When you are up there and it jams or something goes wrong you have nobody else to call on so you really have to be aware of all the details otherwise you'll be in a hole make no mistake. I have fired them on the range and they are very powerful – not at all like anything else I have shot!

In the afternoons we have more classes and then we go up again for a couple of hours in the evening. On Sundays we only do morning and evening flying – there are no classes – and for the last two the weather has not been good enough for us to go up so I have managed to have a couple of rounds of golf. There is a very good links course here which a group of us play. I am doing well as the others are all English and not used to this type of course, especially the wind! It does blow all the time here.

I will definitely go to France now. They are so short of pilots and their need is so great. Already my group is the longest serving here and I would expect to be in France by the summer. I must say I cannot wait!

Thank you for the gloves.

love,

Ted

★ ★ ★

Diary of Nora Anderson, Christmas Day, 1915
Strathairly

The second Christmas of this War. I hope dearly it will not reach the next. The newspapers did not think it would make the last one.

I read the newspapers very little now. On one page they say how well all is going and on the next there are the lists, line after line of men who will never see another Christmas.

Willie has been here for a week, although we have not said a great deal to each other. He talks of his work, how much money they have raised for the Red Cross. He is doing a great deal as he feels he must. He looks tired.

He won't stand for any mention of Them. I tried and he left the room saying we should not dwell on that subject. It is so difficult not to dwell on Them. I do try not to, but how painful it is to see your children sent to the grave before you. It is not natural. I feel horrid pain sometimes, far beyond an aching. Lily tells me I should go and see Doctor McGregor, but he will not be able to do anything for me.

I wanted to see Them buried but we have had no such meagre comfort. We know one was buried and we have had his pathetic possessions. Of his brother, nothing. He lies somewhere and nobody knows where. How do we bear it? Should one 'suffer rather than a nation grieve'?

We hardly spoke over lunch. Lily had done wonders but I had no appetite and Willie eats very little these days. There has been little light all day and it faded quickly after lunch. I suggested Willie took some air. He did not care to and has sat and stared into the fire all afternoon. I do not know what to say to him. He wants to talk of very little. At least he is resting.

It is dark now outside and I can hear the wind. It is making my bedroom window rattle. It has been very windy, and cold too. I have not left the house for three days. I wish I could see Teddie, my little honey bee. It has been such a long time. He writes such happy letters as if he is enjoying the most tremendous adventure, flying through the air like a young knight. I wonder when he will go. I hope they wait until the summer when at least it will be warmer up there. He is so young. He has never been away from me at Christmas before and that is making me tearful. I do not care for weepy women and I will not become one.

I do not know how long Willie will stay for. I hope Hogmanay, as it would be comforting to begin a New Year together. Then I have much to do. The soup kitchen is ever so busy in the winter months and Lily and I will go down tomorrow to help with the cooking and are to go for provisions the day after. There are four widows in the village now and all have children. One has four aged under six. They face a terrible struggle as the Army does not provide much for them, which is terribly shaming. I have written to an officer in Glasgow whom Willie suggested but am yet to receive even an acknowledgement of my letter.

I watch these wretched widows when they come to the kitchen. There is one called Elspeth, who cannot be more than 20, who walks as if in a dream. She says nothing and when there is an inquiry as to whether she is in health or if her child is getting to the school she smiles a small, sad smile and nods without meeting the questioner's gaze. Her husband was in the Gordons. They say she has lost a brother as well and her father is also in uniform but I do not think he is in France.

I have decided that in the New Year I shall return to Glasgow for a time so I can be with Willie more. It would be good to stand at his side. We have to be strong together.

★ ★ ★

Teddie, January 21, 1916
Catterick

Dearest Bertie,

So sorry for taking so long to thank you for my Christmas present and no I have not already read it. I have had little time for books since I moved to Cloudland I can tell you. Thank you also for the gloves – they are a Godsend indeed when you're up!

It has all been very busy, taking my exams and leaving Ireland and getting over here and settling in. I have been here a week now as a pilot. We are not fully-fledged pilots yet as they want us to get more hours under our belt before sending us out, but we are just about ready to fly the nest! If I am lucky I may even get a crack at a Zeppelin while stationed here.

We are a reserve squadron but the CO and a couple of others are experienced flyers and they sometimes help out in the hunt for the Hun when he comes across on his raids. That is always at night which is why they don't let us go as night flying is terribly difficult. It is very easy to get lost.

I passed all my exams – that was why I was so busy over Christmas and New Year. We were sent to Northolt, near London, to finish it all off. I only just got through rigging, but the rest were all fine. We had to take off and do some circuits then land at a particular point. We also had to drop a 'bomb' inside a circle.

I completed my test up here as my posting came through quicker than expected. I had to navigate from here to a neighbouring aerodrome, get the duty officer to sign a chit and then fly back again. I thought I was lost at one point but luckily saw a church and was able to get back on track – I didn't tell anybody that!

I have been higher than 4,000ft now. It is part of the test that you have to be up that high for at least 15 minutes. That was quite a thrill.

There are two squadrons here at Catterick, altho' our squadron is spread out over several fields.

They are good fellows here. Most are English apart from one Canadian, two Camerons and one Argyll. The three other Scotches are all waiting for their postings to France. I told the Canadian all about Ronnie. He is not from British Columbia but has often been there and said it is very beautiful. He is from Quebec.

The weather is grim again today so we are going to have a cross-country run after lunch. We didn't get up yesterday either and everyone gets very grumbly when we sit around all day so the CO has decided on a sporting contest between the wings.

The Canadian says he is very fast but we also have one member of our team who could be said to be on the large side so it will be a close contest and one I must say I am not looking forward to. I always despised running at school and don't suppose my opinion has changed.

Do you think you'll be able to come over one afternoon, or come for dinner and stay at the mess? You would be very welcome and the CO likes to have guests. It really is not that far from you. Please come, I have not seen you for such a long time.

I got a very kind letter from Norman MacLeod congratulating me on becoming a flyer.

I had better go to have some lunch so it will settle before this afternoon's arduousness.

Let me know when you will come and visit.

Please pass on my wishes to Gertrude. I hope all's well with you.

love,

Teddie

★ ★ ★

Bertie, April 4, 1916
Ripon

My dearest G,

It seems such a long time since summer now. And it doesn't appear close to returning either. When will this winter end? This wretched storm hasn't helped. We still have snow everywhere. It did a fair bit of damage to the huts and they have been difficult to repair with the weather still so poor. It does very little for the men's morale. There is little we can do with them at the moment and they are growing restless. There is an air of impatience. Their mood was not improved by the continual trouble on the Clyde. At least the strikers have returned to work, otherwise our men were all for marching up there to make them. Those in the depot that have returned from France are particularly angered and I can only agree with them.

I had a long talk with Bill yesterday. He doesn't think there is any chance I will go out for sometime. I know that will come as comfort to you, yet I feel so wasted. He told me that we are doing valuable work here. These recruits have to be made ready as possible in as short a time as possible, but how can one prepare young men to go to France when one has no first-hand experience of what they are going to? I can instruct them in advancing across open ground under shell fire but I cannot tell them about it.

This is always a bad time of year when spring is late and at present it can only serve to dampen the spirit more than ever. It leaves one cold to read the newspapers. France is bleeding to death at Verdun while Britain strikes and argues over who should be called up to protect our country from mortal danger. It cannot make encouraging reading for those returning from France, or worse standing in a trench over there, and it does not make for good reading stuck here. I do think strikes should be made illegal at once until this war is at an end. It sullies Glasgow's reputation and dishonours all those men from the city who are serving our country. We know that as much as anyone.

I did receive some comfort from Mother. She wrote a long letter which arrived on Sunday. It is the most at ease I think she has been since Ronnie went and much of that is down to Little Ben. His posting to Montrose has come at just the right moment and has really put her mind to rest (if not his – he's ever so keen on getting to France). If it is possible, I do hope you might get over to Strathairly with the boys for a day or two sometime soon, especially if Teddie was to be there. That would make Mother happy.

We have the Brigadier for dinner in the mess tonight – that is not an evening made to improve my mood.

Bill has offered me the chance of a weekend sometime soon. I have said I would think about it and I will let you know my plan, but, my darling, you must understand if I do not take it up as I believe my place is here and I must set the proper example for the men.

With all my love,

B

                   ★ ★ ★

Teddie, May 4, 1916
Bramham Moor

Dear Bertie,

I am for France!! At last I am to go across. I have just heard I go in a couple of weeks, so I have a little more time to get some more hours under my belt and I also have the chance to take some leave. I will spend it at Strathairly. Do you think you will be able to come up at all? I will telegram you the dates as soon as I know them for sure – I hope to begin my leave on May 13th. It would be wonderful if you could come for the weekend at least as who knows when we will see each other again. Unless you too come to France!

I have barely had time to settle in here before getting my orders. I must say when I was posted here I was not altogether happy – my first regular squadron and it is in Yorkshire not France.

My mood was not improved by my journey here either as the train between Tadcaster and York was terrible and it took me an age. When I at last reached Tadcaster they told me I had come to the wrong station. You see the squadron is split between three fields, fortunately they were able to give me a lift over here as the thought of taking that train all the way back made me furious.

The squadron's job is to defend the munitions works at Leeds and Sheffield from the Zeppelin raids and also to intercept them if they cross the coast in our vicinity. They went over here when Glasgow was raided last month. They said it was terrible because the city was not nearly properly blacked out and that is absolutely asking for it. They dropped 98 bombs in all on Scotland I was told. Did Gertrude see any of it?

They have not let me up yet to chase the Hun. We had an alarm the other night but I was told to stay put – most frustrating you can imagine! They send me to France but not up above Yorkshire!

Must go as have plenty to attend to. Please come to Strathairly.

love from,

Teddie

★ ★ ★

Diary of Nora Anderson, May 18, 1916
Strathairly

'Thou wilt not love to live, unless thou live to love.'

My fair-haired, beautiful knight, so kind, so full of joy and life. He alighted amongst us and brought laughter and happiness with him. It was a wondrous handful of days, torn from the darkness to bathe in light. The sun shone to bless us all as spring shrugged off winter's grip and I was blessed with my knight.

He is a joy to me and such is his all-embracing enthusiasm and desire to live that I know he will not be lost over Flanders Fields. My knight must be immortal. He wanted so much to go that how could I let a mother's love dampen any of his warlike ardour? It is my duty to support him as he goes to fight the good fight. If our armies were only all like him, this horrid war would have been set fair for a mighty conclusion in Good's favour. Then all our families could be together once more.

There is much talk of a big push in France and I cannot see any way in which my knight will not be to the fore of it. It will try me, but I am determined to be strong.

I have decided to collect an album of photographs together, for a memory and, I think also, a distraction. We have many of Teddie as a boy and as he grew and I will collect them all in one album so I have a record of his life from baby to boy to youth and now a blossoming young man.

I took them out this afternoon, perhaps as he was even boarding the boat to cross the Channel to France. The first I have is of him at Cowhill in the garden when he was just one. He peers quizzically at the camera but how the camera takes to him. There are many at Cowhill, some with dear Father. It makes me very happy that he knew my dearest little child before his time came to an end. He was a pretty boy. I believe he had a happy childhood and will look back fondly on it in his dotage. We had a happy home. There was always laughter and merriment. Strathairly has been a happy backdrop for a happy family. We will be happy again, I am sure of it. Once time has healed the scars, we shall be. Scars always fade.

Some of the photographs I had not seen for several years. I have never had cause to look back and I have never considered it a useful past-time. Today tho it does bring some comfort to an old and foolish woman. There are many from a late summer at Loch Inver, the boys and their father on the hill and then all learning to fish together. Teddie is already casting while his elders still fiddle with their hooks. That was the last time my family was together. Oh my 'children, tossed to and fro, and carried about with every wind of doctrine by the sleight of man'.

The last picture I came to of that holiday was one of the boys on the little boat, the Gertrude. I remember the day. The weather had finally turned and I insisted they took Kenneth with them as they were not experienced on the water and those sea lochs can change in a moment. They are dressed in capes and waterproof caps and while the others sit and look out on the loch, Ted stands and is facing the camera. He stands out. The others have always been content to see what life might serve them, but not Ted. He has always chased after life, always wanting to be in the centre of every going on. His is a life that promises so much.

My dear Bertie is happy and content with his young family, quiet Gertie and my two grandsons, and he is happy and content to follow in his father's footsteps at the firm. When called upon to do something he will act and do it well, as he is doing now with his young recruits. He is a solid and dependable man. A loving father and caring son. He is so apart from my Teddie. They may be different but they are close as brothers, altho sometimes it can seem more like an uncle and his

73

nephew. At moments Bertie can offer a calming hand and I believe that does Ted good from time to time, as long as he does not rein him in. I do not think anybody could absolutely rein in Teddie, not Bertie, his father, the army nor the flying corps. He is a free spirit and I believe he is destined for greatness, my brave young knight. He will fly high.

'Do not worry about me, Mother,' he said as he stood at the foot of the stairs on his final morning. He was wearing his uniform and I made him come outside and Willie photographed him. Perhaps I knew already that I would want to make up an album. These photographs will take pride of place. He looked splendid in his tunic and cap. Then we made him dress up in his coat which he wears to fly. It is large and leather and has a huge furred hood. His smile shone from his warm surrounds and I forgot our approaching parting for happy minutes.

I did not go with him and his father to the station. I had chores to do here in the garden and Gertie's sister is here, she is an admirer of Ted and rather a keen one at that. So I bade him au revoir and he waved heartily all the way down the drive. Tuppie hurried inside. I fear she was crying, which does nobody any good and I am glad Ted did not see that. I listened to the engine until it was long gone.

McCullum is to leave us to work on the Ross farm. They have no labourers any more, all their young men having gone off to war. Ross had five sons and three have met their fate, two in Flanders and one in Africa. A man came round on his bicycle a week or so ago. He was from the ministry and enquired if we had any able men who could work on the land. I fetched McCullum and he was keen to get off with the ministry man there and then. He does so want to do something that he feels will contribute. He will come back here when he can to see Lily, who is being very brave about his absence, and help us if he has a moment.

In three days time we have all to turn our clocks forward by one hour. The government calls it summer time saving. They say it will help cut the consumption of coal which is becoming more and more in short supply. Then come autumn we are all to turn them back again. It all seems most peculiar, but Willie says it is a good idea, especially for the cities and the farmers too.

He will be in France soon. I prayed for him last night. I prayed that he will be brought safely home to me. O Lord, deliver him from evil.

CHAPTER 8

CLOUDLAND

Teddie, May 25, 1916
Northern France

Dearest Mother and Dad,

I am not allowed to say where I am apart from 'Northern France', but it is a sound enough spot and I am thoroughly enjoying my life out here. I have so much to tell you. We are ever so busy, always up looking over the Hun, that I have had no time to write before now. Please will you pass all my news on to Bertie as I will not have time to write to him at the moment, but do tell him I will send him a long letter telling him everything as soon as I can.

I have a chance to write to you today because the weather is not very good. It stopped us going up this morning and now we are waiting hoping it will clear so we can get up sometime this evening. We have been very lucky with the weather. This is the first morning we have been kept on the ground. We had a huge thunderstorm a couple of afternoons ago but that actually cleared quickly and did not really disrupt our flying.

As I said it is a fine enough spot, tho' not as good as some squadrons have. There is one not far from here who are quartered in a chateau! It is Bobby Loraine's squadron. Do you know him? He is the actor. I don't suppose you've seen any of his pictures. No such luck for us, we are in huts but they are cosy enough and we have everything we need at the field.

We usually go up twice a day. The first trip is very early and we are all up before it is light and taking off as the sun begins to rise. When I arrived they were keen to get me up straight away. I went first to a large depot not far from Boulogne where I landed and then they sent me forward to here. I got here in the afternoon and they had me up that evening. I was taken to see the CO – a fine man named Major Burdett – and he told me all about the squadron, what we do and whose flight I was to be in and then I was taken over to my machine where my fitter and rigger were waiting. We are each given a fitter and rigger to look after your machine – and you! They say you become a little family – they are the most important people to you as they keep your machine from falling apart. No sooner had I said hello than I was told the briefing was about to begin for the evening patrol, so I had to rush to my billet and pull on all my kit and rush over to the briefing.

One of the other pilots told me to give my machine a thorough going over before going up. Lots of men have been killed by a faulty machine rather than the Hun. So the four of us – me, the rigger McEllen, who's from Nairn, the fitter Johnson and Will Begg, my observer – pour over the machine. It is a BE2c, which I do not have much experience on. They had them at Bramham Moor so I was lucky to have at least been up in one. When the check is done Begg and I clamber in. A mechanic shouts 'switch off', you reply 'switch off, petrol on, air closed, throttle open' as loud as you can – it's some mouthful. The mechanic shouts out 'contact' and I yell back 'contact' and switch on then he gives the propeller a mighty heave and we are ready to go.

That first one was a fairly gentle sortie up to the line for a look around and then back. I got a good look at the front and have seen it everyday since, apart from so far today. Once you've reached your height you head east and below you France is laid out as if a patchwork quilt, like the old one in the nursery at Strathairly. From our height there are at first no signs of war and the countryside is wonderfully green. Then you catch sight of the trenches. The two fronts are easily spotted with just the naked eye. They look like the battlements on Edinburgh castle and stretch out in either direction out of sight. They are a brown scratch from up above and behind them you can see the zigzagged lines of the support and reserve trenches. In between the two lines, no-man's land looks lush and undisturbed, everything has grown untended by human hand – as nature intended is what Major Burdett says – through spring and summer. Around the trenches you can see craters made by the shelling but from up here they look like the worm casts Mother used to complain about outside the greenhouse at Strathairly!

It was odd seeing the trenches for the first time, they looked so insignificant and besides up above we have other things to worry about.

Archie has been the main bother so far. That's what we call the fire from the Germans on the ground. I have not yet come close to seeing a Hun machine, on my second time up we saw a flight in the distance but they didn't come near us and quickly disappeared. They are very cautious the Hun. They never come across our line, whereas we are always going over theirs and causing all sorts of nuisance. They try and nuisance us with Archie. The first time took me by surprise but you soon get used to it and it never frightens me. You are flying along when all of a sudden you will hear a sound like pouff, pouff and these white clouds will burst around you. When you are over the Hun lines you must change your course regularly so their gunners can't get a fix on you. If they are very close it might make the machine wobble somewhat, but not even as much as flying into a cloud, and even if you are hit you might not notice at all until you return home and the rigger begins patching it all up. Begg told me I must take great care when landing as you may have no idea that you have been hit and the damage it might have caused the machine, so you don't want to come roaring down in case the whole thing collapses around you.

I have learnt so much since coming out. I really think it is the best way to learn all about aviation, being out here with these men. My navigation has improved enormously already. We have a golden rule. If in doubt fly west, which makes it ever so easy if you do not know exactly where you are – just look for the sun. The roads that were built by Napoleon (I remember from history that he built them on top of the Roman roads) are also jolly useful as they go straight on for miles and are a great help in finding your way about.

At night after we've all got back we all sit around in the mess and talk about flying. It really is a wonderful place to learn. It is not all about flying tho', they are a very relaxed lot and we talk about all sorts. There is a piano and sometimes everyone will sing popular songs. Begg is very good to me – we shall be a good team I think and I have become friendly with Tom Scaife and Jack Coats. Tom is from South Africa altho' he was born in England.

Mother, you really must not worry about me over here. I am having the time of my life. On my second patrol I saw the famous 'Virgin of Albert', I'm sure you will have read about her in the paper. We were at about 8,000ft on a bright, clear day and it made for an astonishing sight with the sun reflecting off it. It looks as if it will fall any moment as it is leant right over. The saying goes that when she does fall the war will end. Yet it doesn't say in whose favour!

So don't worry. We live well here, indeed the food is considerably better than anything I have had since I joined up. We see the papers regularly so can keep up with all the news. Our billets our comfortable and we are in a much better state than anyone else out here.

I will write again soon and tell you more about what we are doing.

I include a photograph I had done in London on the way out. It was taken near Hyde Park. I am in my Flying Corps uniform and cap. I did not care much for London.

With all my love,
Ted

* * *

Teddie, June 6, 1916
Northern France

Dear Tuppie,

There is no flying today so it gives me a chance to write all my letters. I have received so many since I came out which makes life much more pleasant. Thank you for all yours, it is a real joy to get them. I have also had letters from your sister and parents as well as my brother (your brother-in-law!) and parents and Norman MacLeod (do you know him? He worked in the firm with Bertie), Frank Donald, who is back home for the time being, and George Harvey. You will recall them from summers and holidays at Strathairly.

I am sorry for not having replied to any of your letters until now but we have been very busy and it is only when the weather turns bad that we have a chance to do things like write letters. If the war was fought in Scotland we'd be writing all the time! Here in France it has been a splendid summer since I came out. We have had a few drizzly days but this is the first on which we have actually been grounded all day. It is raining hard and the clouds are very low, which is the particular problem as that means our visibility is reduced to just about zero so it is of no use to anyone going up.

Yesterday we were practising with the infantry so it was a fairly straightforward day. We have to spot where they have advanced to and then fly back to HQ and either drop a message or radio their whereabouts to the staff (you see not all our machines have radios yet – don't tell that to the Hun!). We have also been practising spotting targets and then telling the gunners where they are. They are always keeping us busy. I have become an expert at reading a map. You have to be able to pick out features in the landscape and when most of the front is one great indistinguishable mass it can be very difficult to spot just what's what.

I am tired as you do have to concentrate so very hard all the time, but it is the most enormous fun and terribly interesting. Apart from getting up at four o'clock for the dawn patrol! We just fall out of bed and pull our kit on over our pyjamas! You would not recognise me by the time I am all kitted out, eyes peering out from behind my mask and covered from head to foot in fur and leather – I bought an enormous flying jacket in London on the way out (which I wear instead of the one with which I was issued back home). I had been saving my pay as one of the experienced fellows at Montrose had told me they were an absolute must, and he was right. It is absolutely sweltering when you're all wrapped up on the ground but once you get up you soon appreciate it. Then it's into the machine, everything checked and ready and off we go, the noise of the engine drowning all other sound as we hurtle over the grass, then, before you know it, she is skimming above the grass like a huge bird and you tug the nose gently back and head for the heavens!

It is a splendid sight to climb into the sky as dawn arrives, I wish you could see it. We climb and climb and then head east for the front. It doesn't take long before we can see the trenches, brown scars in the summer green. It is strange to think what is going on down there, and the horrors of it all. When it gets quieter I mean to go to the front and see the trenches first hand. I also want to find where Ronnie is buried and I have written to the graves people.

Once we cross to the Hun side we are given our wake up call. Pop, pop, pop and puffs of smoke, white clouds like pulled cotton wool will surround you. Archie's awake – sometimes the bursts are white and other times they are black which tends to alarm you more, just because the colour! But we largely ignore it and carry out our duties and before you know it, it's time to head west again where breakfast awaits!

It is as if we live two lives. We have our military lives when we fly and are always watching out for the Hun or targets or taking photographs or looking out for angry Archie, but then once we are down and have filled out all the dreary reports we have quite normal lives. It is rather like school. There is lots of ragging, we play sport (the field is a wonderful space to hit golf balls but we only have a couple of clubs and five balls between us. Perhaps you could send me some for my birthday?) and we read and we eat well and then have hot baths and beds to sleep in. It is much more a usual life than those in the trenches have.

There are soldiers all around us, many, many battalions, some you have never heard of, and soldiers from all over the Empire. Sometimes we will have guests from other battalions for dinner in the mess and they are always very envious of us.

I have taken to drinking wine. We always have it with dinner and it is very good in France. I try not to have too much as rising at dawn with a heavy head is not at all pleasant. Tom Scaife, Jack Coats and I normally have just a glass or two as we dine, but others do take quite a lot and then start singing and playing the piano. One of them does a very good impression of Harry Lauder! You would like Tom and Jack. I have told them all about you. Tom shot down an Albatross before I came out.

Jack won our bombing competition we had yesterday. We are practising dropping a new kind of bomb but of course we cannot use real ones! Instead we use a dummy, made of wood and carved into the shape of a bomb. We only have one so we take it in turns to go up and try and drop it on a target marked on the field. To add interest one of the flight commanders suggested a shilling-sweep and it soon became a sizeable bag (Bertie would not approve!). I went up second and hit the target successfully but not absolutely in the centre. Jack then went up and landed it in the middle. There were amusing incidents later, the next man up just missed our quarters and later the wing commander arrived unexpectedly to watch the competition and narrowly avoided being on the receiving end himself. He was not impressed when on the next go the dummy was dropped into the canal that runs alongside the field thus ending the contest!

Later yesterday afternoon, after the bombing comp, we made the short trip to the village of L'_____ , which has received a terrible bashing from the Hun. It was Jack's idea as he wanted a go at this game he had heard of from a chap he was at school with in the next door squadron. It's called wall-pushing. In towns and villages near the front there are lots of walls left standing on their own in the ruins and the idea is that you try and push them down with one hand, or two if you must. They come down with a resounding crack and bang. It turned out to be a wasted trip. The Hun had done such a thorough job on the village that there was not a single wall worthy of the name left standing.

Jack has just come in (I am writing this lying on my bed in my hut which I share with Will Begg my observer) and told me that we will certainly not be flying at all today so this afternoon we will go into Amiens and look for Charley's Bar which is where everyone goes and try and have lunch at the Oyster Shop which is said to be very good. Tom has been before.

I must close now as I have to write to Dad.

love,

Teddie

★ ★ ★

Teddie, June 26, 1916
Northern France

Dearest Mother and Dad,

I hope you are both well. I am in the rarest of health and have been kept very busy up in Cloudland.

I see in today's paper it says in the official communique "We destroyed five of the enemy's kite balloons yesterday" so I suppose I am at liberty to tell you about it, having taken part in the destruction. In my letter to Dad I think I told you I had been practising dropping a new kind of bomb for destroying balloons. Well Jack Coats and I each carrying 48 of these and accompanied by another type of machine carrying a species of rocket, set off to strafe a Hun Kite balloon, commonly called a "Sausage". These are captive balloons which are sent up from a good way behind the trenches to watch the result of their batteries fire and to try to see the enemy guns firing. A little balloon at the back keeps it steady and facing into the wind, and the observers sit in a little basket underneath.

The aeroplane with the rockets was to attack first, then I was to drop my bombs and then Jack Coats drop his.

This was to happen to all the "Sausages" on the line at the same moment so that they would not have time to pull them down after seeing another come down. We started off for our balloon which was about five miles behind the German lines at the appointed time. When we approached the balloon, Archie got very busy and the air was simply thick with them bursting all round. Then the machine with the rockets which was much faster than we were, dashed away ahead, down to the level of the balloon, while we had to remain about 3,000 feet above it (i.e. about 7,000 off the ground) to give our bombs time to get well lighted. He fired his rockets and hit the balloon just as I was going to drop my bombs because I thought he had fired and missed. The balloon just disappeared leaving a ball of flame with a trail of black smoke behind as it dashed to earth. I was not going to return with all my bombs so I dropped them on the Huns who rushed out to the remains of the "Sausage" and Jack did the same with his!!!

Poor defenceless sausage!! It was a huge golden affair, and disappeared utterly!!

The Archies attended us on our homeward journey and were fairly good shots too. I enjoyed it all immensely, and felt so "bucked" that I sang lustily most of the way home!! When I looked over the machine on landing, I found six little Archie holes in the wings so they were quite near. It is peculiar that you never notice how close they are when you are up.

They got too near Jack Coats this morning. We were up on a patrol for the gunners when he was hit by Archie but it is nothing serious and he should be back with us soon. I was able to see him before he was taken away and he was in fine spirits.

The sausage affair was the best show we have had since I came out but all the work is interesting and there is an awful lot of it. I have counted that I have been out here for 36 days and on only one day have I not been up at least once.

Our main job is working with the gunners, that's what we spend an awful lot of our time doing. Once we're up – Will Begg is still with me as my observer – I circle while he unwinds the aerial. That takes about 15 minutes as you can't do it too quickly in case it snaps and then you would have to land and repair it. When it's all out we check it works and Begg will put the drums on his Lewis gun while I begin climbing to the height we will work at which is normally about 7,000 feet, altho' if the weather is bad we will go a lot lower so we can get beneath the clouds.

When we cross the lines we start looking for our target, call up the battery and then keep instructing them until they are on target. We are Archied nearly all the time, but you really rarely notice it. Sometimes one will burst next in front of you and it will feel like being in a small boat when you hit a wave – imagine being in the Gertrude on a stormy day on Loch Inver! Other times it makes your stomach flip, like how you felt when Ronnie drove over the hump of a Wade bridge somewhere up in the glens!! But then it's back to concentrating on the ground and watching the flashes of the explosions.

Watching the barrage from up here is a remarkable sight. The air is full of shells and so we are always bumping about – you can feel quite sick with all the buffeting! You can see the pin pricks of light that are our guns firing and the blasts of the explosions on the Hun side. It's a frightful sight and I would not care to be a Hun at the moment.

The barrage has been going for a couple of days now – no doubt the papers have it that even in Fife your breakfast cups are shaking such is the intensity of it! – so it is no secret that the push will come soon and we shall be busier still. The Hun really are for it, if you could have seen what I have over these last weeks, the men and might that we have, well it fills you with the greatest confidence.

love,

Teddie

Ps. Please tell Bertie I met a couple of officers, Millar and Sharp, from his old battalion in Amiens. They asked after him and wished he could be out here with them and not left to follow it through the papers back home. They are going to take part in the push and said the battalion was raring to go. They will do Glasgow proud I am sure.

CHAPTER 9

ATTACK

Diary of Nora Anderson, July 2, 1916
Strathairly

It has begun. Willie has gone back to Glasgow to prepare. He said there will be plenty of wounded men to come no matter the success we meet and more funds will soon be needed. It's all the talk in the village, although there is little actual news. We know it has begun but that is the extent of it. Of course, there are rumours and talk already of large advances by our men and the Germans retreating. I do not know what to make of it, but I do know that the lists will be long when they appear in the newspapers.

Willie has made me promise to take a newspaper tomorrow for the first news of the battle. He said that I must keep myself informed of the situation, it is my duty to do so. So tomorrow I will send Lily for a paper.

I think of Teddie a great deal and I thank dear God every night that he is not in the foul horrors of the trenches. My young Knight will come through having played his part in the greatest Battle history has known. It may bring him home soonest. May it be so.

I search for distractions. Outside the sun is shining and I can hear Colin, our new boy, whistling a tune as he attends to the vegetables. I must remember to instruct him to tell Mr Robertson to keep a newspaper for me when he returns to the village this evening. Colin is a good boy. He works with such enthusiasm altho he has told me his real enthusiasm lies in joining up. He has tried already, taking the train to Edinburgh so nobody would know him and presenting himself at the first recruitment place at Haymarket. His youth, tho, is too apparent. I told him to be patient and his time will come, poor child.

July 3, 1916
The Times, London

FORWARD IN THE WEST
START OF A GREAT ATTACK
FIERCE BATTLES ON THE SOMME

Long awaited news of a great British offensive reached London on Saturday morning. An attack had been launched north of the River Somme at 7.30 that morning; British troops had broken into the German forward system of defences on a front of 16 miles and a French attack on our right was proceeding equally satisfactorily.

Yesterday our aeroplanes were very active in cooperation with our attack north of the Somme and afforded valuable assistance. Three of our machines are missing.

The great offensive in the west has made a good beginning and promises exceedingly well, but an operation meant to be prolonged cannot be judged on the results of the first day or two.

THE GREAT BATTLE
SPECIAL ACCOUNT
THE BIGGEST BRITISH OFFENSIVE
from our Special Correspondent
British Headquarters, Saturday

At half-past seven this morning a great battle began on a front of about 25 miles above and on both banks of the Somme. Perhaps it will be known in history as the Battle of the Somme.

The fighting is of the most desperate character and will probably so continue for days. At the moment it is only possible to say that we got our first thrust well home, and there is every reason to be most sanguine as to the result. While not being understood to be in the nature of an attempt to force a final decision, it is the biggest offensive that the British troops have yet undertaken.

OUR MEN MARCHING UP
As we stood in the shadow of some trees, 20 yards from a road which led directly down to the trenches, detachments of our troops

could be seen swinging across country. Long before they came close one heard the steady roar of their feet – tramp-tramp! tramp-tramp! And always as they passed they whistled softly in unison. Some whistled 'Tipperary' some 'Come back, my Bonny, to me' and some, best of all in the place and surroundings 'La Marseillaise'. One felt their presence and heard more than one saw them; always the steady tramp-tramp, tramp-tramp as they shouldered by; and they were always whistling. Now and again a laugh broke out at some unheard joke, a completely careless laugh, as of a holiday-maker.

And knowing what it was they were going into, for the 50th time one marvelled at the way in which British manhood has proved itself in this most terrible of all wars.

It was a lovely summer morning, the sun, still low, shining directly in our faces from behind the German lines. Albert was almost hidden in the mist, except that the church tower, with the wonderful spectacle of the leaning figure of the Virgin, stood clear above the white bank below and gleamed golden in the sun.

The advance was set for 7.30. When 7.30 came the mist was too thick for us to see our men advancing from their trenches. Faintly, straight ahead of us, we heard through all the clamour a ripple of rifle fire. And all the while, above the smoke and mist, two kestrels swung and circled and hovered in the sunlight.

It has turned now into a beautiful summer day, with promise of great heat, the first that we have had for over a week. The sky above is a clear blue, flecked with dazzling white islands of cloud. But over there, where at night the horizon was all a flicker of lightning, there is nothing but a sullen bank of thick pearl grey. Behind that bank the British Army is winning new glory.

The place was a veritable devil's cauldron, a mere bowl of seething fumes, black and green and white. Nothing is yet known of what the issue was; but it seemed incredible that anything, friend or foe, could live there. To us, looking on, it was the sight of pure horror.

I have already alas seen many of our wounded. It is impossible, however, at present to speak of the battle, otherwise than to say it has only begun, but begun very favourably for us. Only by degrees will it be possible to see the whole thing in anything like a true light.

★ ★ ★

July 4, 1916
The Times, London

A LONG BATTLE AHEAD

It is now possible to get something like an accurate picture of the results of the first day's fighting.

In the first place, our artillery fire had over most of the front been extremely destructive and very good. As always however, there were places where individual bits of trench and stretches of the protecting barbed wire had miraculously escaped. Some of the latter caused our attacking infantry considerable casualties.

Another point to be mentioned in connexion [sic] with the German resistance is the immense strength of their machine guns. Wherever their resistance has met with any success the chief factor in that success has been the survival of their machine guns in impenetrable positions where our bombardment could not reach them. In several cases such guns were able to play on our troops as they came from the trenches, doing considerable damage.

It is no time yet to talk of "victory" but we can assuredly claim great success.

★ ★ ★

July 5, 1916
The Times, London

DESPERATE STRUGGLE

From our Military Correspondent, Paris
The first British attacks won many important points, but against a series of strongly defended villages in the German line our artillery preparation was less effective than was hoped, and the German masses appear to have been placed in movement early. Here, as in England, everyone realises the struggle will be desperate before definite results are gained.

From Our Correspondent
Our great new Armies are better than we can have dared to hope. Nothing has in any case stopped them except being killed.

Our losses, of course, in the whole battle will be very heavy. But already one is tempted to say that any losses are justified, not merely by the defeats which we hope to inflict on the Germans, but in teaching us the magnificent quality of our men who are not professional soldiers, but are British people. The essential thing is that to-day we have at no point gone backwards or failed. Of course there will be checks and temporary reverses but our confidence everywhere is complete. The day could not have gone better.

★ ★ ★

July 8, 1916
Glasgow Herald

A letter to Glasgow from Lt Col David Morton, commanding officer, 17th HLI, France. He writes:

I should like to express to all relatives of those who have died, my sincerest sympathy with them in their present great sorrow, and to assure them that all the remaining Officers, NCOs and men share their grief with them.

It may be some consolation to them to know that the battalion walked into action as steadily as if it had been on the Parade Ground, and I cannot adequately express my feeling of admiration for the spirit, gallantry, and daring with which all faced their terrible task.

Those who have, in this battle, given their all for their country, did so in a spirit worthy of Scotland's best traditions.

It may be a comfort to the relatives of the wounded to hear that all who came in contact with them testify enthusiastically to the patience and fortitude with which they bore their sufferings, and to know that the spirit they displayed very greatly increases their chances of rapid recovery.

I have always been very proud of my Battalion, but in the action of July 1st, Officers, NCOs and men, one and all, displayed so much coolness, courage, and resource, that my pride has been more than justified.

Yours very truly, David S Morton,

Lt-Col, Cmdg 17th HLI (Glasgow Chamber of Commerce Battalion)

★ ★ ★

Teddie, July 14, 1916
On the Somme

Dear Dad,

I'm sure you will have seen all the papers. We have been in the middle (or should I say above) it all and have seen the whole event unfold. It is a sight I will never forget. What a manner in which to celebrate my 20th birthday!

We have been up every day until today and at least twice on each day. It is most awfully interesting work and I would not have missed it for anything. We have to fly low and pick up signals from the infantry by lamp etc and drop messages at Corps Headquarters giving whatever information we have obtained as regards Huns, their artillery etc.

I was up about two hours after the attack, by which time the Hun lines were in our hands and the attack on the village of M_____n was beginning. I saw the attack and capture of the village which was of course intensely interesting. We were down at about 1500ft most of the day and were not troubled by Archie at all, but were rather badly strafed by Hun Machine Guns, and our machine had to be sent away as unfit as there were so many holes in it. The GOC of the corps for which we were working was very pleased with the work the squadron did and wrote a very nice letter to our CO.

The attack is still going strong, the French doing splendidly, and our two Corps on their left getting on slowly but steadily. Further north the Huns are putting up a better resistance.

Yesterday I had the satisfaction of knocking out a Hun battery. I saw it firing from a wood and came down quite low. Looking through glasses I saw the three guns and about 20 men standing round. So I flew off and sent down by wireless the position of the battery to the Corp Heavy Artillery and about 20 minutes later had the satisfaction of seeing it blown up by a direct hit!!

It seems as if the artillery have never stopped firing and there is always the thunderous noise of the guns. How the Huns withstood it all I do not know, but somehow they did but our attacks will keep going on. The barrages the gunners have put up have been incredible to witness. We have to watch we don't get brought down by our own side as the air is thick with shells!

As much of our work has been at a low level some of the barrages are at our height and you can see shells passing and then watch them all the way as they fall away and even see the flash as they crash into the Hun lines. Below it looks a sea of volcanoes. Tom Scaife swears he saw one shell actually reach the height of its ascent and then turn its nose towards the Huns and hurtle down to earth! He said he could have reached out and caught it!!

The weather has turned rather miserable since the glorious days at the start of the month. We haven't been up today as it is very wet and the cloud is just too low for us to be of any use whatsoever. Whilst we are all keen to get on with it, it has at least allowed us some respite and a chance to sleep!

Everything has got rather muddy and it must be a horrid slog in the trenches. You do see rather a lot of names you recognise in the lists. We have lost some of our own from the squadron but you really mustn't dwell on it.

Don't worry about me, I am absolutely fine Dad and happy as I could be flying. It is actually quite a wonderful existence.

Please give all my love to Mother and I hope she and you are both well.

With all my love,

Teddie

★ ★ ★

Bertie, July 15, 1916
Montrose

My Dear Norman,

How are you? I hope you are coming through all this well. I read that all is going according to some sort of plan but the lengthening lists in the papers do suggest otherwise. Thankfully I have not seen many Camerons, but I did see James Bisland was killed, as were Alex Begg, George Gilroy and Alfred Raeburn. All went within a couple of days of each other.

I cannot imagine what it must be like for you over there and you cannot know how much I detest sitting here, once again besides the sea, whilst you, my brothers, my friends and companions give their all.

I saw the dreadful letter in the Herald from David Morton. We were told that he considered writing a public letter to the Herald the best thing to do as it will take many days and weeks yet before all the individual letters of condolence can be penned to wives and families. There were so many of their names in the columns today, men alongside whom I marched out of Glasgow with, men who I had grown with, schooled with, worked with and then trained to go to war with. Then they went to war and now so many will not come back and here I am left to train others to do what I have not and go where I have not. It is not always easy to face them.

Even my father and your cousin are of more use than I. They keep the firm running with barely a semblance of staff and also find the time to do war work as well. I spend hours at my desk pushing through the piles of paper that appear to drive this army.

Forgive me for writing to you like this when you are there in the trenches facing the enemy but you are my dearest friend and there is no-one else I could say this to. It would just worry Gertrude if I told her how much I long to go out, whilst Teddie still sees the whole do as a tremendous adventure, which I suppose does no harm at all. If he can keep that approach throughout it is all well and good really. He appears to be doing ever so well with the RFC and has really taken to flying.

If there is anything you might be able to do to help me get out I would be enormously grateful. I have written to everyone I can think of, more or less pleading to let me out. I wrote to Ian Hamilton but received a very curt reply.

With all these dreadful losses I am sure my time will come soon.

You will be pleased to hear that the firm continues to do well. We have 22 men in service which I think is something we can be proud of. We should also be proud of my father and your cousin who have worked like Trojans.

Do take care.

Your friend,

WH

* * *

Diary of Nora Anderson, July 21, 1916
Glasgow

It is dawn. The light is just beginning to spread into my bedroom. Soon I will be able to turn the lamp off and write by natural light. I long for news and I long not to hear anything, how strange I have become.

It is everywhere. When you step out into the street, the city seems abuzz. Somebody always knows something and like in Fife people cluster around shop windows where notices are posted, although of course here the crowds are much larger. The newspaper boys are always crying out that in their pages is the absolute latest news from France. The noise assails you. I am not keen on the city anyhow and this can make it seem quite intolerable at times.

Glasgow is a strange beast. I don't think anything could still this city. Willie feels at home here. I do not any more and dearly wish to return to Strathairly, but I must remain to be at his side during this time. I think he finds he can distract himself here, whereas when he comes to Strathairly time can stand still for him. He is not a man of contemplative mind, or one who likes to explore the depths of reason. He could not indulge himself in a fine novel for an afternoon, or walk the gardens. He is a man of purpose and that is to be admired. Yet sometimes there are moments when I want more. It is selfish of me, especially in these times, but I too need my comforts, however scant.

I am prepared tho to fight my own good fight – I know it must be done. We all have our wee battles to be won, and it serves the greater good if we fight them ourselves and do not attempt to call the attention of others, who have much larger issues to face, to one's wee woes.

Today I shall go out and walk the streets and walk proudly through this great city that has sent so many of its sons in answer to our country's call. It is my family's city and so it shall still be mine. It was in this room that I gave life to my family and it is in this room that I resolve to be dutiful to them forever.

It is because I am tired that I have all this running through my mind. I am not sleeping and think I may consult Doctor MacKay today.

Or I may just walk for longer and that will tire me and then I should sleep. I want to have a good walk into the city as I have not done much since arriving.

I have noticed that there is not as much in the way of provisions in some shops here as there is back in Fife. Yet there is no complaint, altho Willie has mentioned that there is talk of discontent in the dockyards along the Clyde. Rents have been increased by many landlords and with their men away, many of the women are having difficulty in paying. Willie says business must go on as much as possible – that proclamation

'Business as Usual' is still much in evidence – but he has sympathies for these people and said some most unflattering things about some of the landlords, one of whom the firm actually act for.

Willie was most talkative last evening. I think it was Teddie's letter. It was addressed only to Willie and altho I did not particularly care for that I suppose my Honey Bee is a man now he has left his teenage years behind and there will be manly things he wants only to share with his father.

After dinner instead of retiring to his study he asked me to sit with him in the drawing room and when we were seated he read from Teddie's letter. I know he did not read it all and I cannot but help wonder what he chose not to read. He writes that it is a wonderful existence in Cloudland (which is his name for it) and he sounds happy as he could be.

He would not have mentioned anything to his father I am sure, but I also wonder if he is forming a tender attachment to young Tuppie. Bertie tells me they write each other often. I suppose Teddie feels he must have a sweetheart now he is no longer a boy and I'm sure it must bring some comfort, yet I do not think it is altogether suitable. It was not all that long ago that we believed that she and my dear C were to announce an engagement. She gives the impression of being rather an impetuous young lady, altho ever so sweet. I wonder if I dare mention it to the Gilmours. Or perhaps Bertie could talk to Gertrude, as I think they are close as sisters despite the difference in years. I know how Tuppie does look up to Gertrude.

There were reports of German counter-attacks in yesterday's papers and it seems as if the Big Push did not make the expected gains after all and here I am writing of my son's affairs of the heart. Should I banish such triviality at such a time? It seems this war has a way to stretch yet and people have to go on living, do they not?

Oh, how I long to see my young knight. Will he have changed? I expect he will seem a deal older and probably a bit off with me as happens when a boy first becomes a man and tries to cut the strings of their childhood. In his letters he betrays no signs that this experience has left its mark. He has such an optimistic, happy soul and Bertie thinks if anybody may come through this all without a scratch it will be his young brother. Just to see him, even for the briefest of hours, would make me so happy.

★ ★ ★

Diary of Nora Anderson, August 20, 1916
Strathairly

My Strathairly. Home at long last. The house felt cold when we returned this morning. Cold, quiet and empty. But we have been at Lansdowne Crescent for sometime and Lily has only passed in and out of the main house. I believe a house has to be loved to become a home.

Lily has spent most of her time helping with the soup station, and she has done wonders in the garden as well. We are quite the small farm now and she uses the vegetables every day to make the soup.

Colin has gone. He joined up, altho he was still below the age. Lily said he went to Edinburgh again one day and this time never came back. It was his mother who told Lily that he was in uniform, altho Lily thought as much. She said he's an artilleryman and I will write to Bertie tomorrow for him to tell me what it is like for them so I may inform Colin's mother.

We put a fire on this evening and are thankful we have a good supply of wood still from the old tree McCullum cut down at the foot of the garden. That seems an age ago, and I suppose it was. Lily tells me McCullum has become Farmer Ross's right-hand man and is highly regarded indeed. She was very proud when she was telling me.

I am glad to be home again and I think a few days here will be of much benefit for Willie. There are some days when he does look an old man. There are some days when I feel an old woman. I wonder if Willie looks at me and believes me to have aged. Does he still see the woman he married? I look for that man and I see only glimpses.

At least being here might refresh me. I will take a deep breath and be strong again. There is so much more I can do here than in Glasgow. I felt my nerves there the entire time and all the rain we have had over recent days did not help. The city was greyer than ever. When this is all over I am determined to persuade Willie to take a step back from the firm, let Bertie take up the reins and then we can both live here in our dotage. Bertie and the children would not be far away and would visit often and so would Teddie.

He will come home in time. His youth will demand some adventure and I think he may first want to take in the world beyond all this, but I am sure he will then come home.

Now we are back here I intend to stop reading the newspapers again. They are really too much. In the last two weeks alone I have seen the notices of two boys Teddie schooled with. He summered with Norman Martin on Skye once. Young Scott it said was in the hospital for a month before his time came. What unimaginable suffering!

★ ★ ★

Teddie, August 23, 1916
On the Somme

Dear Tuppie,

I am coming home!! I have been given a week's leave and just have to do my patrol this evening and tomorrow morning and then I will pack my bag and head for Boulogne. I have telegrammed Mother and will make straight for Strathairly. Do you think you will be able to come over and stay? I am sure Mother would not mind and I think Gertrude and the boys will be there. I also hope Bertie will get down from Montrose for a time. I cannot wait to see everyone. I will be sorry to leave here even for just a week but it is nice to be able to have a rest as I am rather tired.

We have been as busy as always and are giving the Huns no respite. Yesterday a Hun machine flew over our neighbouring field and dropped a note that said 'Please give your bloody Flying Corps a rest'!! (Do you mind me using strong language? That is how we all talk out here).

The country is a sight where the fighting is going on. Remember I said it looked so green when I arrived in France? Well, it doesn't now. It is a horrid, churned up brown mess and all the roads that lead up to the front cut great brown scars across the land. It is so different and it is not always easy to make out the actual lines of each side. The entire area is covered in shell holes and sometimes a line is made by just connecting a number of the holes. It only needs a little rain and such are the amounts of men, machines and horses squeezed into this corner of France that the whole area becomes a giant mudbath.

A couple of days ago we went forward to have dinner with the artillery unit we have been working with. They have to put up with terrible conditions and were rather a dour lot which is most excusable given where they are but made for a rather awkward evening. We were shelled just as we left as well.

But the attack goes on and there is still a feeling we can break through before winter. I have been doing much contact work which means we fly low over the lines and look out for where the infantry have got to and then fly back to HQ and drop a message. Some of the men wear mirrors or large bits of coloured tin on their backs so we can spot them and know which unit they are. It means we get a grandstand view of the attacks but also attract a deal of attention ourselves. The Hun can shoot at us with their rifles and Machine Guns and our machines are often a frightful mess by the time we get back and we have to be very careful when landing. The worst thing is to have your wheels shot from beneath you and it is not always possible to tell until you are actually landing. The first thing you know is when you hit the ground with a mighty bump!!

There seems to be an attack of sorts every day so up we go each time. It is sometimes a relief to climb away from the earth and leave all the horrors behind. It is an uplifting feeling to rush into the sky and greet the dawn or say hello to the sun. I would so like to take you up in a machine when it is all over. I think I may stay in the Flying Corps as I am so well suited it to it, so I should have the chance to get you up. Would you like that? It might be quite terrifying at first but I am sure you would enjoy it. We could fly over the Clyde and Glasgow and then out to Woodbank and I could take you so low you could see into the bedrooms!

Did you see the Prince of Wales was taken up? A fellow from another squadron took him and there has been a terrible fuss and he was nearly court-martialled poor chap. It was in the papers.

It is dreadful about Reggie Smith. We went shooting to Bisley together. Two others from Fettes have also gone, Norman Martin and Robert Scott. Did you know them? I did.

I have been told where Ronnie is buried and mean to go there when I come back. When the winter starts there will be more days when we can't go up so I should be able to find the time. I want to try and get a camera whilst I am home so I can take a picture of his grave for Mother. She would like that.

It was Charlie's birthday last week, yet nobody has mentioned it. Nobody mentions him anymore, or Ronnie. It is strange. I miss them.

I suggest you telegram Mother as soon as you receive this letter about coming to Strathairly – do come.

I have to go now and start dressing for the evening patrol (it takes an age) but then I will pack tonight and hopefully leave straight after breakfast tomorrow. Then I can catch the leave boat in Boulogne and should make London in time to get the sleeper. I have not made a reservation as apparently no one bothers any more as there are so many soldiers on board that everyone just grabs what they can.

I will see you very soon.

All my love,

Teddie

★ ★ ★

Diary of Nora Anderson, August 31, 1916
Strathairly

I looked at him closely when he arrived. There was a moment as I stood on the steps and watched the motor pull up the drive that I feared for what it contained. I wanted the boy who had left here those long months ago to return, but I should have not let such foolish thoughts fill my mind. They are the whims of an ageing, weak woman. I cannot banish them, yet I must keep a check on them.

He would have changed anyhow – he is becoming a man, growing away from his youth and even had he been away only to study or travel he would have changed by his return. I need only recall how much Bertie had altered to become a man after he returned from his studies in France.

Yet I fear I have become weaker in these hard times and I believe he looked altered. His face is no longer soft and I could not see past his eyes any more. They were guarded. Will that be ever so? I believe not.

Still tho I can be a mother to him and I embarrassed him with my greeting! I am sure it irritated Willie too!

And after I had him Home and he had a night's sound sleep in his bed, it seemed just as it always was. I was his mother again. I was determined it would be so. Oh! it was a joyful home again. A handful of days sent from heaven. We all came alive – Strathairly came alive and danced once more. And He was at its centre.

What Joy and Happiness unconfined. I wanted to hold on to every passing minute and not let go, but how the days hurried by and when it came I did not want to say farewell to Him, for "In every parting there is an image of death."

Be safe and come back soon.

CHAPTER 10

ATTACHMENTS

Bertie, November 7, 1916
Northern France

My Darling,

We are now in Brigade reserve and will be here for another couple of days before we go back for another spell in the line. I am sorry I have not written before now, but I had no sooner sent you that last letter from Etaples when I was ordered to join up with the East Surreys and the day I arrived with them we went straight into the line.

It has not been an easy start as it is difficult going straight into the trenches with men you do not know. I am only now beginning to remember names.

It was a difficult tour for all concerned as the battalion's ranks have been swelled by the likes of me over the last few weeks as they suffered terribly on the Somme in September. They have been out here since the start of the battle and the survivors have some particularly gruesome tales to tell. They have had a horror of a time. They lost their CO to a bad wound when they led the attack on Delville Wood in the final big push in September.

By the time it was over they were left with only six officers and the adjutant, Lt Clark, who won the Military Cross, was the senior surviving officer. He believes they suffered no worse than many other battalions throughout this dreadful summer and, as he ruefully pointed out, one man is able to see with one glance what we have gained for such a cost. So we are practically rebuilding a battalion, having to start again creating a unit from a mixture of men.

I had never thought how difficult it must be in that regard for COs out here. Back in Scotland with the 17th and then the 19th, they were nearly all men from Glasgow and its surrounds, so naturally there was an easy air of comradeship about the whole battalion. I did notice how that began to change as our ranks became stocked with those who had been at the front or were from different places, but when you get out here and suddenly have to mould a battalion out of so many disparate elements it is a substantial task. Added to which one is aware of not being part of the original regiment and, despite being a senior rank to everyone but the CO, I have not experienced what the others have.

Most of the men are from the southern reaches of England, but they are really no different to the men of the 19th. If anything they tend to converse more. The officers are mostly very young and confident products of England's well-known schools. I am not altogether sure they appreciate having an old man from Glasgow telling them what to do!

I do find it difficult not to take a fatherly approach to them. There were times when we would be sitting in our battalion headquarters dugout and a group of the young subalterns would be chatting away about this or that concerning the latest news from London, whilst I sat in the corner and puffed on my pipe feeling every inch the benevolent uncle. How strange!

I think of that de la Pasteur quotation I used to so like: 'No generation is in perfect touch with another. Each stands on a different rung of the ladder of time – you may stoop to lend a helping hand to the younger, a reach upwards to take farewell of the older. But there must be a looking down and a looking up, no face to face talk is possible except on the same level – no real and true comradeship – the very word implies a marching together. How can we who have to be commanding officers of the young be their true companions'.

Does that hold true? Now I will find out for sure.

At moments of quiet I did start letters to you, but there were constant interruptions as it was a busy baptism for the old uncle. I have those letters but have decided to start again with this one as then I can tell you everything that went on a bit more clearly.

There will be no secrets. I promised you that (so long ago it seems an altogether different world) so here is the tale of my life here.

We went in on the night of the 31st into a sector that is not too bad. Our HQ dugout, where I lived, was comfortable enough tho' inevitably a little damp. Everything up there is and despite thinking I was prepared for it after everything poor old Ron had written and Teddie and others had told me, it still came as a shock when dawn came on that first morning and I saw where we were. My the mud. It is a scene of desolation everywhere. Not a tree or anything of the sort in sight.

I peered through these periscope contraptions they have which stop one having to poke one's head over the top and the scene that greets one is pretty much indescribable. In front of both trenches are great forests of wire and in between nothing except shellholes and barren ground. At first it leaves one speechless and wondering just how anything can survive or live out here, but then the noises of everyday life infiltrate one's consciousness and one sees the men going about their lives in their cheery manners and soon enough I was part of that too.

The dangers are real enough, but those who have seen it before help us newcomers through and it does not take very long before one feels a veteran of the line, tho' with that is a peculiar unease that is more or less a constant accompaniment. It is hard to describe, perhaps a feeling of being slightly queasy, or a nagging doubt about something or other in the back of one's mind, as if one's forgotten something but can't ever be absolutely sure what exactly.

The first couple of days we were in the line were trying as the shelling and such forth was pretty constant. Most of the shelling went over our heads, in both directions, and once one is used to the noise it does little more than gently fray one's nerves, altho' I do not look forward to being on the receiving end of a proper shelling.

A greater worry is the smaller stuff the Hun are prone to hurl at us. They were very active with their aerial darts throughout our stay. They are horrid little things which do take one absolutely by surprise and they can be very vicious. A more measurable threat comes from the 'whizz-bangs' which the Hun do seem to revel in chucking at us. A cry of alarm will go up as the noise signals another impending arrival and one hurls oneself into the mud and one's mouth and nostrils fill with France – believe me I am getting to know Madame much more intimately than I ever did in my student days at Tours. There is a terrific bang and the splinters fly everywhere. Then it's over.

It lasts barely a few seconds and then everyone jumps up and makes vain attempts to brush off the omnipresent mud. Someone will unveil a smile stoked by bravado, make a crack and we'll all howl with laughter and then get on with our duties, the moment passed. It is almost a game, whether one is an oldie, like me, a young subaltern or gnarled sergeant, you don't want to be the one to duck first – all for different reasons, but I suppose they are essentially all the same at heart. One does not want to lose front. I do especially feel so as this is not my regiment and I am still very much a newcomer to the men.

It is remarkable in a way that my actual duties as a second in command out here differ very little from those back in Ripon or Troon. This army still survives on paperwork, even out here in the very front line within a stone's throw of the Hun. One has to account for every piece of equipment on the battalion's front. When we come into the line we inherit all the clutter from the previous battalion and that has to be checked and listed ready to hand over to our replacements. Every plank, duckboard and roll of wire has to be accounted for. We have to check we have the number of waders it says, or picks and shovels and if the numbers do not tally we will soon receive a call from brigade demanding to know what has happened to three shovels and so on.

One evening in the middle of an intense burst of Hun whizz-banging I was called to the telephone to speak to a staff officer insisting we tell him how many size seven boots we had been issued with for each company before we came into the line. When I got back from my tour of the companies with the figure they wanted, Clark told me that two days before they went up in September they had been instructed to find out the average number of children per man in the battalion. It's really quite extraordinary.

Apart from my tasks at HQ I have tried to get out round the companies as much as possible so I can get to know names and faces and they can get to know and see me. The lot opposite were quite jumpy throughout our stay and so these visits were often lively. Even in the quiet times we have one company CO who delights in winding up the Hun even if it leads to retaliation. He is a young captain who was one of the six to survive the September attack – came through completely unscathed despite being in the thick of it throughout. I have the impression he feels he is untouchable now, which I also think makes his men wary as he is always volunteering his company for everything and insisting on leading it himself. A remarkable young man and one is loath to try and curb his instincts, especially as he has been out so much more longer than I.

Anyhow one morning I was with his company for stand to. That turned out to be uneventful and after the men stood down and began preparations for breakfast I decided to head back to HQ. But Captain Clarke said I should wait for a spot of morning sport. Soon enough we see the thin fingers of smoke from the Huns' breakfast brews rising into the sky. The captain and one of his snipers take aim at the Hun parapet above where the smoke is coming from and unleash a volley of shots. This left me puzzled and when they did it again a little further down the line I was still none the wiser. After they did it a third time, the captain said to me we should seek some cover and sure enough a minute or so later a little barrage of darts crashes into our trench. There were no casualties and the men dusted themselves down and got on with making breakfast. Still mystified I asked the captain to explain. And with a great smile spread across a face that looks much older than his 21 years, he told me that it was their way of stopping the Hun enjoying their breakfasts. When they fire at the parapet they believe it ensures the Huns' food is sprayed with mud and dirt thereby making it even more unappetising or ruining it completely! The force with which they reply convinces him it works. It may not do much to win the war, he said to me, but at least it makes the Huns' life as uncomfortable as possible. I did have a word with the CO, but he believes it is all for the good of moral if nothing else.

On our third day in the line, three Hun machines flew low over our trenches and we unleashed a terrific barrage at them. Then two of our chaps arrived and sent them hurrying back to their own lines. We see plenty of machines in the air everyday and I often wonder if one of them might be Teddie. The subalterns are all frightfully impressed that I have a brother in the RFC. The pilots are all seen as terrific heroes, which I shall certainly not be telling Teddie – imagine his ego then!

We are set into the system now and shall spend a time rotating in and out of the trenches. We are unlikely to have to spend as long as Ron did in the line in one go, as it is all much better organised now, so altho' one is constantly tired we always have a rest to look forward to.

Try not to worry, I am sure I shall be all right. I feel I have at last settled in and am getting to grips with my job. Mankind does have this incredible ability to adapt and I do not find it overly terrifying now I have a degree of experience of it all, all I hope is that I do not fail. I would, of course, have preferred to have come out with my own regiment, but I so wanted to actually be out here that I must not grumble. I am devoting myself to the East Surreys and that is that.

I enclose a letter to each of the boys, please read to them for me!

Write soon, my love.

With all my heart,

Your loving husband,

B

★ ★ ★

Teddie, November 18, 1916
Northern France

Dearest Mother & Dad,

I am sorry not to have written recently but we have been having a fairly grim time of it. I did ask Tuppie in my last letter to let you know what little news I have had.

Did you know I am now back with my original squadron and am very glad to be so? I was with the other squadron for a month, it was much the same work and they were decent enough, but it is not like being with your own squadron. The CO was Harvey-Kelly, who back in 1914 had been the first RFC pilot to land in France. It was not a pleasant month, the weather was, and still is (we are grounded today) awful, and we suffered heavily as well.

They have been suffering here too. I am sure you saw Tom Scaife's death has been confirmed. We are all saddened to lose him. He was a terrific fellow and I believe I shall miss him tremendously.

Earlier in the week we had a wireless operator killed and another wounded, while yesterday John Barry was wounded. They have had a tough time of it – the field was even bombed by the Hun.

We are all so glad of a break today. The benefits of leave wore off very quickly and once again I feel tired. I have not been sleeping so well. One of the joys of poor weather is that some mornings the dawn patrols are cancelled or delayed and we are granted a precious few extra hours in bed. It is most peculiar really as we are all tired and a little shaky, especially before we go up, but as soon as you slip into your machine and lift her towards the heavens, the fatigue disappears and you feel ready for anything.

I still find the work interesting and now with the Hun more active we have to be even more alert. It is a real challenge flying in the winter. I have been up in much worse conditions than I had ever experienced before – even in Ireland! On one particularly bitter morning my observer's face mask froze over and he couldn't see a thing! You are aware of the cold when up, but it is not until you land that you really feel the effects. Some days I have to be helped out of the machine I am so numb, but a quick nip and then a hearty breakfast soon has the body functioning!

I went on my first bombing raid while I was attached, but the whole thing was rather a chore. It was a miserable day, raining heavily and so it was difficult to find our way, but we did, dropped our bombs and came home again. The rain was so heavy we could not even tell for sure whether we had hit our target. It was nothing like the balloon raid. Because of the weather we have been doing some low level flying over the Hun lines and support lines to give them a good straffing. It is a good way to lift the spirits. Captain Summers, my flight commander, had his machine fitted for dropping grenades, but he had to scrap the idea after one exploded in the rack and nearly brought him down. He only just made it back to the field and that was the end of that experiment!

Otherwise it has been more contact and cooperation patrols, all of which are extremely difficult in this weather. When the sun at last came out towards the end of my month on attachment, we lost two machines and their crews in three days. It is never pleasant to arrive at breakfast or dinner to find two more chairs gone.

It rained constantly throughout the final few days of my stay and I was so glad to take my leave in the end and come back here.

There are a few new faces, but enough of the old ones still remain to make me feel at home again.

I read in the papers that recent days have been uneventful over here. Well, the fat correspondent who penned that should come and spend an uneventful day with us. I do sometimes resent what they write in the papers. It is either nothing happened or some death or glory tale about the Scouts. We wretched old Corps never get a mention, yet the work we do is most valuable and just as dangerous. I saw that 60 machine set-to that they wrote so much about over Baupame. It was some sight but it is the everyday tasks that are the real achievements. It does make me angry,

Dad. Shooting down a couple of Hun doesn't in itself advance our cause, whereas spotting a Hun battery and then guiding our guns on to it does so much more, not least for Bertie and the poor devils down below.

Ian Macdonald has gone, he came out with me, altho' he had been in the trenches before. He was at Festubert when Ronnie was there. I suppose he is with Ronnie again now.

I saw Patrick Monteith has been killed. He was another at Fettes, altho' I did not know him well. I knew his younger brother Matthew. He went in July.

The rain has stopped but the clouds are still very low so I cannot see us going up at all today. Part of me wants to, indeed most of me looks forward to getting up there again where you can breathe and live life to the full, but there is another part that wants the clouds to come lower still and keep us in our beds, just for a day's rest. One day is all it would take to get all of us back on our feet.

At the other squadron there was an officer who had been with the East Surreys, not Bertie's actual battalion but the regular one. He said Bertie's lot were a fine bunch and he should have no trouble there. That is heartening to hear. I still have no news as to how he is. Do let me know as soon as possible. I am going to write to him now.

I hope all is well at home. It is so nice to have more photographs with me now. I can look at you and Strathairly whenever I desire.

With love,
Teddie

★ ★ ★

Bertie, December 18, 1916
France

My darling,

We go back into the line tonight but hope to be relieved before Christmas. The feeling is we may have it just right. If the Hun keeps quiet, which apparently the Saxons are prone to do over Christmas, we should get out on Christmas Eve and be back in billets for the morning. Whether it happens remains to be seen but it is a comforting thought as we prepare to go back up. Let's hope we are opposite the Saxons and not the brutish Prussians.

The CO has decided there should be no leave for anyone over Christmas. He thinks that is the only fair thing to do and he has the support of all at HQ.

It will be strange to think of you and the boys on Christmas Day. I do so like Strathairly at Christmas, especially when Mother has the house covered in her decorations and it is full of the sounds of children and the excitements of the season. We shall have a celebration of sorts – whenever we do get out of the line. The battalions have to decide whether they are to mark Christmas or the New Year and this is the moment when one does absolutely notice the difference between the Scots and an English battalion. Nearly all Scots regiments have chosen to celebrate Hogmanay, 'us' English have gone for Christmas.

There will some sort of festivity – the CO is keen for the quartermaster to lay his hands on a barrel of beer for the men, which the QM, a rotund little man from Worthing, claims is the most difficult task he has ever been handed in the Army.

Yesterday I was making my way back from brigade when I came across one of these non-combatant battalions. One's opinion of them has always been on the low side, and as I was passing the Hun chose that moment to drop of ton of hate on us so we all dived for cover and I found myself in a hole with their commander.

Now I can't call him an officer, or give him a rank as they have none. Everyone is addressed as Mr So and So. They have no badges either. He was a talkative fellow and seemed most unperturbed by the shelling, peeking over the top every now and then to shout encouragement to his men to stay under cover. At first I did not want to talk to him but he was persistent and broke me!

He was a history graduate from Oxford who had been a teacher. I asked him how, as a student of history, he was not prepared to fight for the cause of right. He explained his reasons at length – far too long to go into properly here and if I were to shorten them it would not be fair – and whilst I do not agree with them (and thank God that more do not hold their views) and told him so, at least he is prepared to come out to France and do something unlike the shirkers one sees everywhere at home.

They work as labourers and he told me they get given extra meat rations because of their work. I did not agree with that at all, but I suspect he may have been pulling my leg. He says none of his men smoke nor drink and they all work tremendously hard. I asked about casualties but he said they have not suffered one apart from through 'certain' diseases. Perhaps they are not so saintly after all!

When it all quietened down we parted on pleasant terms but I don't think either of us had changed the other's mind to any great extent. Nevertheless an interesting half hour and good again to exercise the mind at something other than War!

I must say we have not spoken very much about all the changes, but in general I do tend to agree with you. Now I know before all this I would have struggled to find a good word to say about that Welsh scoundrel but we certainly need a leader who can galvanise the Government. I have not been impressed with their efforts and would not either have backed Bonar Law to take over. I do not believe he is the inspirational leader we need right now. He was certainly never very popular in Glasgow circles before the war. Not leadership quality was the widely-held opinion.

The French papers are calling Lloyd George the 'English Genius', which I'm not sure he would absolutely appreciate! He has been very well received over here, the man to lead the masses they say. (Writing about the French papers, it occurs to me that I have not yet spoken to one French person, nor have I spoken a word of the language.)

The peace note has been received out here much as you say it has back home. I think the Herald got it right in calling it the 'Devil's truce'. It is reported that the Kaiser has said that his army has won a victory and that is why he is now calling for the peace to be determined. Well, from my position out here (however uncomfortable!) it does not look like any sort of victory that history has witnessed before. I see the note said it would be for the "benefit of civilization" to call a peace, but the greatest benefit to civilization would not to have started this whole horror in the first place.

The CO had me read out the "note" (as it was published in the Times) to some of the men and not one of them thought it was anything other than a German ruse.

It has turned cold here now. When the sentries come in from the saps the men have to rub them and swaddle them in blankets to warm them up before they can even talk. Winter here will be a weighty cross to bear I feel, but the spirit of the men is so wonderful. I really can't explain how close the bond is that is formed amidst these horrors that we live through out here.

It is especially noticeable among the ranks, for with officers there is more movement between units, but the men they largely stay together. There are some here who joined up together straight from their workplaces and have come through the Somme together. Their ranks are, of course, thinner than they were. Everyone out here knows loss. Yet they go on, cheerful and accepting of their lot in this life of filth and mud. Men grumble – and they have plenty to grumble about – but it is always accompanied by a joke and you rarely hear a real complaint. Scots, English, Welsh, Irish, Canadian, Indian, French, Australian they are at heart all the same. Being out here has an effect on one's beliefs and opinions and in some ways it is an experience I would not have missed for the world. If it were not for missing you and the children I could truthfully say I am glad to be out here. It is something every man should be tested by.

I have always tried to identify with Shorthouse:

'That all men are really alike, that all creeds and opinions are nothing but the mere result of chance and temperament; that no party is on the whole better than another, that no creed does more than imperfectly shadow forth some one side of truth; and it is only when you begin to see this that you can feel that pity for mankind, that sympathy with its disappointments and follies and its natural human hopes, which have such a little time of growth and such a sure season of decay'.

It is a sentiment that is easy to agree with, but not always easy to practice. I do not think I have practised it, until now and being out here has helped me to really understand it and believe it.

Now here's something you will not so readily believe. I have been cooking. For whatever the men here can do, one thing they most certainly cannot is cook and it has moved me to take up the wooden spoon. I forgot to mention it in my last letter but on the final night of our last tour I cooked for HQ. My servant is a fine man but an awful cook, so I relieved him of his duties and stewed up corned beef for the CO and adjutant!! They said it was worthy of the finest restaurant in Glasgow so I had to chide them for their London airs! I stand by my abilities but I have been relieved of my duties and been ordered to hand the spoon back to Wilson from tomorrow. Most insulting!

My darling, I do not think you should worry overly about Allan. Greece is something of a backwater and I have heard the Bulgars are not much interested in making trouble and are quite happy to just sit there, each to their own trench. The weather will certainly be much kinder for your brother than for us wretched unfortunates over here. I know it is easy for me to say do not worry, but truly you must try not to. It is not good for the body to worry, it will wear you down. You must protect your health. If nothing else, you must think of the boys.

I have had a rush of letters in the last few days. Norman is on the mend, whilst Frank and George are both well and pass on their regards. If we are out for long enough and go back to reserve rather than support I do hope to see Teddie at some point over Christmas. I worry for him as he has been out a long time. I had heard that it is usual in the Flying Corps once they have done six months or so they are often returned home for a break as an instructor. That would lay Mother's mind to rest if it were to happen. And no doubt Tuppie's too!!

I will try and write again before Christmas, but if I cannot have a Merry Christmas my dear and I am sure we will be together for the next one and many more after that.

With all my love,

B

★ ★ ★

December 27, 1916
London
To: Anderson, Strathairly, Fife
IN LONDON. ON SLEEPER TONIGHT. HOME TOMORROW. MEET ME AT STATION. TEDDIE

★ ★ ★

Diary of Nora Anderson, December 27/28, 1916
Strathairly

It is late and I cannot sleep a wink. I have never in all my years suffered such an assault on my emotions. I want to write it down and try to make sense of it, but I do not know if I can write. I need to calm myself.

I have counted 12 days since I last wrote. My hand is shaking. I will stop and have a glass of water.

I was here in my room, ready to prepare for bed. Lily knocked on the door. I had not heard the telegram boy. Normally you hear the wheels of his bicycle on the gravel. Perhaps he walks at night as his bicycle has no light. I had not heard a thing, I do not know if he even rang or knocked before Lily answered. Perhaps he went to the back door. Lily knocked on my door. As she spoke she looked at the ground and only looked up at me once she had finished. I think she was too scared to see my reaction to her news.

A telegram, late into the evening. I stood up, trying to keep myself straight. As soon as she had started speaking a picture of Teddie had burnt itself in the forefront of my mind. He was all my eyes could see. I tried not to think, yet I could not stop rushes of thoughts. I may have been dizzy and Lily supported me as I took a shawl and walked down the hall to the top of the stairs. My heart ached. Willie was in the hall, the telegram opened in his hands and as I took the first step, Lily coughed gently and he looked round. He smiled up at me and I knew relief.

I have not seen him smile like that for such a time. At once my heart was no longer aching, now it was bursting. Your favourite boy is coming home, he said to me. That smile was still there and I thought I would fall but Lily held me.

My darling boy, my young Knight, he will be here in the morning. I do not think I shall sleep tonight and this is an occasion I do not begrudge it. I have not been happier since the day I brought him into this world.

Willie wanted us all to go straight to bed so we would be fresh for his return. I would not let them and commanded that we must decorate the house as we always have for Christmas. I commanded that we shall have Christmas after all. Willie went to bring the decorations out and Lily and I attended to his room. We sang carols as we made up his bed and Willie came to see what all the fuss was and he smiled again as he saw what we were doing.

Bertie told us that it was normal for pilots to come home after a six-month turn in France and I pray this is Teddie's turn and this is not only another leave. Surely, he would not be granted another leave when his last was only a few months gone. I have never heard of it before.

I believe he will be home for lunch tomorrow – indeed, today, for it is today. Willie will telephone the station first thing and then go down to meet him when we know the time of his train from Edinburgh and Lily and I will go to the village to unearth a feast fit for our returning Knight.

I wonder how long he will be with us for. I do not know how I would cope with him returning to France again. Willie said that there is a shortage of pilots and experienced men are wanted to prepare new ones. He thinks that's where our Knight shall go next.

I expect he will want to see young Tuppie and I will telephone Woodbank tomorrow and invite her for the weekend. I also want Gertie to come with the boys to see their fine uncle. We shall have a belated Christmas. It will cheer Gertie up some and I believe that we have fortune again and next Christmas we shall all be here, Bertie as well, and Strathairly shall come shining out of the darkness.

★ ★ ★

December 30, 1916
The Times, London

Field Marshall Haig's Somme dispatch
Conclusion
Verdun had been relieved; the main German forces had been held on the Western front; and the enemy's strength had been very considerably worn down. Any one of these three results is in itself sufficient to justify the Somme battle. The attainment of all three of them affords ample compensation for the splendid efforts of our troops and for the sacrifices made by ourselves and our allies. They have brought us a long step forward toward the final victory of the Allied cause.

Our new Armies have proved themselves, to the enemy and to the world and in the fierce struggle they have been through they have learned many valuable lessons which will help them in the future.
Ends

CHAPTER 11

ROUTINE

Bertie, January 6, 1917
France

My Darling,

Happy New Year. A thousand thanks for the parcel – it has made for a very happy mess!

We have had quite a time of it since I wrote to you on Christmas morning. And I am now 35! I have been very fortunate that we had both Christmas and my birthday out of the front line.

We lost four men as we came out on Christmas Eve, but at least on the day itself we were untroubled and able to have festivities of a sort. Under the circumstances it was as good as it could have been. Then on my birthday the quartermaster excelled himself and turned up a decent bottle of wine which we shared whilst polishing off the cheese you sent and most of that whisky too.

Who would have thought the English would be such avid whisky drinkers! I should think the distillers are secretly rather fond of War! I certainly am a regular Scotch man now and I have never been overly fond of it in the past. You must remember that, my dear, when I telegram ahead of coming home!

All in all an interesting way to turn 35!

Anyhow they were a welcome few days of respite but the next day we went back to the front. This is a particularly lively area and we have had a hot time of it, none more so than the way I welcomed 1917. If you could have seen me! I was wading through thigh-deep mud and slush in a communication trench trying to get back to battalion HQ when the Hun decided to greet midnight with a vicious salvo. Our gunners did the same so we had a tremendous firework display for some time and I had nowhere to go except huddle at the side of the trench in all the mud and make what progress I could. It took me an age and I made quite a sight when I finally made the dugout, much to the amusement of the other occupants! Muddied but unscathed!

We were in for six days and they were all very active. We were shelled from dawn on New Year's Day and battalion HQ was hit by gas shells which made for an uncomfortable few hours and it didn't calm down until after lunch, but fortunately we didn't suffer any casualties.

The shelling, whether it be from the artillery, or minnies or darts or trench mortars, is fairly constant now. There are days when it can feel intolerable, even if it is no different to the day before and what is sure to follow tomorrow. I don't know why one has bad days, but after our New Year's treat my hands were shaking. The next day we had much the same but I was calm throughout. I suppose one's nerves do get worn down to an extent. Sometimes it doesn't do to think about these things too closely.

On our last day, yesterday, the CO had an extraordinary escape. He was on his rounds with his orderly when he narrowly missed being hit by a minnie. The CO was somehow unscathed and so was the orderly, altho' the poor chap was buried up to his waist and was badly shaken by the whole thing. Minnies are nasty brutes, altho' if one is alert, or the sentries are on their toes, they can be spotted in plenty of time and one can 'make haste' in the opposite direction.

All in all we were relieved to come out last night and thankfully the handover was a quiet one. We are in the support lines now and our dugout is not a good one, especially in this miserable weather. We will be here, with much work to do, for several days before we go back to the front again.

That is the routine one is used to now. There are days which stretch for an eternity and others which hurry by in a blur of explosions. Sometimes one feels the dull days are more trying, especially as we sit and shiver in our holes. It wouldn't be so bad in summer when it is warm and dry – those who were here then talk almost longingly of those days (altho they are happy to ignore the likelihood that it is then that we will no doubt be sent into battle) – but it is so difficult to keep warm and impossible to stay dry.

I hope I don't paint too grim a picture for you, my dearest, but I must be straight with you. It is what we are, is it not? The truth: the foundation stone of us. I do not want this to come between us. Others here talk of how strange they feel when they go home. They say they cannot talk to people at home as they do not understand. They say that in a way they feel more comfortable out here till it is all over. This they can understand and no-one who has not been here can; being at home only angers them as they come against a wall of ignorance built by armchair generals and one-eyed newspapers.

This must not come between us, that is why I do tell you everything as you have implored and hide nothing from you.

Remember Lennox Coyningham's saying … 'As there is a heaven above you, so there is a hell beneath you.'

We have always to be aware of that, especially so in these times.

I am always thinking of you.

With all my love,

B

★ ★ ★

Teddie, February 3, 1917
Kent

Dear Bertie,

I hope you are well and surviving life in muddy old France.

I have been posted to the Artillery Cooperation Squadron and sent off here where I shall in due course take over a flight I think. I am then to be an instructor for the time being. I don't mind doing it for a while, and of course I would not turn down the chance of a promotion – I am catching you up! – but I do not want to be here for too long and want to go back to my squadron eventually. I think instructing for too long could become very trying.

It is strange to fly again without being shot at or having to keep a constant watch. I do anyway, I suppose I will always be like that, and you must stop yourself falling into bad habits. It would be no good to get used to not keeping a keen watch and then find one's self back in France.

I have been doing a lot of photography and have sent some pictures back home. I also had one taken of me standing in front of my machine which I have posted to Tuppie. When you next come home I will show you the pictures I took from the air. After the war I will do one of Strathairly. Of course it is much easier to take the pictures now as flying in a straight line doesn't matter with no archie about so you can really concentrate on leaning over and making sure the camera is properly readied and targeted and not have to keep a hawk eye out. Try convincing the trainee pilots of that tho'! They think it will all be enormously easy.

We haven't been up much at all since I arrived as the weather has continued to be bad. We have had plenty of snow and the clouds have more often than not made it a complete waste of time to go up, and it is too dangerous as well for the pupils. We have had a number of accidents, two of the more experienced pilots had a head-on collision over Wiltshire and both were killed.

Have you had snow out there? I can't imagine it is very pleasant over there at the moment. Do you think you will get leave anytime soon? If you do you must come here on your way through. It is not all that far from London and I could take you up for a flight!! I am sure you would be better than some of the pupils we are sent!

It was so good to get home for a few days and see everyone. You know no-one has changed, apart from my wee nephews! They have really grown – I think you will be surprised when you see them. Mother did flap some tho. She made such a fuss of me it was almost too much. I could see Gertie was laughing at my embarrassment, and I fear Tuppie was as well. I do wish Mother would realise that I am a grown up now and should be treated as such. Has Gertie said anything to you? As for Dad, well, he is still Dad.

When I came back I did not know where I was going next and when they sent me on to a reserve squadron I was not happy. When they first said I was to come here I was not happy either but Major Dowding explained it properly to me, and I think I can achieve much here, altho' I did ask him that I should be sent back before too long.

I wonder if you can become battle rusty being back here? I shouldn't have thought they would want to risk that happening to experienced pilots.

Before I came down I had a weekend in London. The RFC have opened a club on Berkley Square and altho' those recuperating have priority I was able to wangle a room so passed two nights in tremendous style. One night I went to a show – not a very good one actually. On the

Saturday I went to one of Jean Hamilton's afternoons for the wounded. Most of them were in chairs the poor devils and they don't say much. All the ladies, young and old, fuss around them and want to know about what they did and how we are giving the Hun a good seeing to, but I find their continual bright-eyed enthusiasm wearing and looking at the fellows I think they are the same. It is not easy to talk to people.

I found it difficult seeing Tuppie at Christmas. It was awkward and I didn't know what to say. It is easier to write to her in letters. Did she mention anything to Gertie? You must tell if she did.

Write soon and tell me all about life with the Surreys.

Love from,

Ted

* * *

Diary of Nora Anderson, February 7, 1917
Strathairly

Gertie tells me she thinks Bertie is finding the winter difficult to cope with and she does worry so. I think it is she who is finding the winter difficult to manage. I am reassured that she now spends much of the time at Woodbank where her mother can fuss over her and the boys. I tried to do so throughout their visit, but I did find it difficult. I become tired much sooner these days it seems. Doctor MacKay has given me what he terms his potion to help with my sleep but I do not feel it does much good and anyhow I am loath to have to rely on anything like that. My sleep will come back when all returns to normal, and so I must make do in the meantime.

I fear tiredness does make me short sometimes and I was not how I should have been with Gertie and I believe that is the reason we squabbled. She and Bertie are so alike and she is just as stubborn as he. I feel she believes (she all but gave voice to it) that I care only for Teddie and have forgotten the rest of my children. Oh, that angered me and I had to leave the room.

It is an untruth. I watch for Ted as I am all he has. Bertie has her and the boys. Bertie is a man, Teddie, my golden young Knight, is barely such and I fear for how He has been snatched from boyhood and hurled into manhood with no pause. The horrors he must have witnessed at a time when the world is still new and wondrous to him, Oh Lord, it makes me grieve for Him at times.

But now He is home and safe and it is Bertie alone who is in danger. I pray for him each night and he is always close to my thoughts and always next to my heart. Yet he has Gertie, as Ted has me.

I saw a horror of my own the day before we returned from Glasgow, which was a very chilly trip on the motor. This really has been the most awful winter. It is sometimes difficult to concentrate my mind, yet I cannot readily recall such snow and cold, and the wind just whistles to my bones. Willie took me to see the arrival of a wounded train. He goes often to Queen Street for his Red Cross duties and has always said I should see one. He believes everybody should see one, from mothers to strikers, as only then can one realise the true duty we citizens have to support those out there in France and beyond.

It was a dreadful sight. I do not think some of the men had been washed or had their clothes changed since they had been taken off the frontline. Willie said that when the trains first started coming in crowds would gather and applaud and cheer the poor men as they limped past or were carried to the ambulances, now those that do come just stare in muted horror at line after line of ragged, bloodied wrecks of men, or boys in some cases. Some looked no more than boys. One, who in appearance was no more than 16, was crying for his mother as he lay on the platform on a stretcher waiting for the attendants to take him away. His hair was caked in mud or his own blood, I could not tell which. He made me think of Colin. We have heard no news of him for a long time – I intend to send Lily to ask his mother tomorrow. He was only a boy.

After they are unloaded and lie on the platform waiting to be taken away they are comforted by young volunteer nurses, many of whom themselves are little older than girls. Mrs Williamson's daughter became a Vad recently and was sent to a hospital in Ayr where many wounded are sent from Glasgow. She was very pale when she came home on her first leave and would not speak to her mother of what she had seen and now I have some idea just why.

It was not a restful time at Lansdowne Crescent. Willie says the war has finally reached the people of Glasgow. He believes it will become worse unless the Americans finally enter the war. When they do the end will come quickly, he says. I pray that they will come soon.

There is less and less on view in the shops. At least here we can find rabbit. McCullum has been sending us some from the Ross Farm and Lily has even taken to making expeditions into the fields about the house in the early morning armed with Willie's shotgun and accompanied by an eager Lad. She has yet to find any success. She blames Lad for scaring them away before she can take aim. She is much better at teaching me recipes for rabbit and I have made quiet a success of rabbit pie.

We used the last of our vegetables for the visit of Gertie and the boys. Everywhere seems to be running short and the soup we have been helping with for the village kitchen is not as nourishing as it needs to be for those poor children. The numbers who attend have grown again.

I have started doing meatless suppers on several evenings as the Government has recommended. I do not think Willie cares for it and he looks like a young Bertie as he reluctantly chews on his potatoes and vegetable stews. It makes me smile.

The newspapers urge us to eat less but in this cold that is difficult, especially for somebody like Willie who is forever busy and on the go. The nurses also need plenty.

Willie's health did concern me for a time, but now he seems fit and well. His spirits vary, as all ours do. I know he writes long letters to Ted and Bertie. Ted writes much less than when he was in France, although I think he still corresponds regularly with young Tuppie. Gertie tells me the pair are quite taken with each other.

I have reached a decision to write my journal entries longer but on fewer occasions. It is ever so cold and we are being urged to save fuel and black out against those dreadful zeplins [sic]. One was sighted coming up the Forth when we were in Glasgow, everybody claims to have seen the monster, and I told Lily she must ensure we are blacked out. I will go to bed earlier to help save on our fuel use. I will miss my late night writings, they have been a huge comfort and there is much less time, and peace and solitude, in the daytime so I will have to set aside particular moments to write my journal.

Jean asked me at lunch on Sunday if I had persisted with it and was most surprised when I said that I had. She did not believe that I would and when I pressed her, she declared that she never thought of me as the type who could write. I said that I did not think I was either, but I did not like being called a type.

★ ★ ★

119

Bertie, February 13, 1917
France

Dear Norman,

We are out at last. Ever since I arrived in France we have been in and out of this dreadful area of the line near H_____ – I am sure you will know of where I am talking about. Even being in reserve was unpleasant, but finally we have been moved right back to rest billets and this morning I had my first bath for just about a month. The relief you can well imagine; I have never appreciated a bath so much.

I am now sitting in my warm billet, clean and content with a full pipe and a proper dinner – or the nearest we'll get to a proper dinner – to look forward to and time to catch up with all my correspondence.

I am sure you will have a battalion soon and I do hope you get one with the Camerons. I do not think it would be easy going to take over as a stranger. It is surely better to promote the second-in-command, don't you think? And that is not just because I am a second-in-command!

I found it difficult here to begin with, especially coming into a unit who had been through so much together and I did feel very much the outsider for some time. Now tho' we have been through a testing couple of 'routine' months and I feel much more settled.

It is all so different to what we knew in the Territorials. In truth I don't suppose anything could have prepared one for this. Those days do seem incredibly distant. As does working for the firm. In quieter moments I think of going back; how strange it will be. Can you picture yourself suited again and striding down George Street!?

Father often sends me details and keeps me informed of the firm's affairs – he says he has written to you as well. I know it must be difficult for them too, having to carry on as normal when all this is going on. They are doing a very good job and, who knows, if the Americans come in then we might be back at our desks before we know it and be bemoaning how dull it all is! I tell you tho' when it is over that will definitely be the end of my soldiering!

Since the turn of the year I have had enough soldiering to last me a lifetime. We have had a very odd lot opposite and they have been active too, as have we. One day, when the sun made its first appearance of 1917, a German got up behind his trenches and just started walking around until one of our snipers bagged him. No more appeared after that, but that night there were shouts and whistles from no-man's land followed by a small explosion and then shrieks and groans.

The next morning two Germans appeared on the parapet of their trench. One quickly dropped out of sight, but the other ran for some distance along the parapet and then jumped down out of sight. Moments later he reappeared waving a flag. I was in the front trench and saw the whole thing. Once he had waved it around he jumped back down into their trench. It didn't seem right to have a shot at him.

We had reports that they were heard digging for most of the rest of the day. The following day I was called down to the line again by a bemused company CO – there was what sounded like a brass band playing in the Hun trenches. It went on for a while and then stopped. We were more than usually happy to move back to divisional reserve that night.

When we next went up we were given instructions to mount a raid, the major purpose of which was 'to secure a sample of German ration bread'! The CO contacted Brigade for confirmation and we got the same message back. It fell to me to plan the event, the first time I have done so for real. It had to take place in daylight. We got what they wanted, bread and three prisoners. It cost us three dead.

On the way back one of the sappers was wounded and so another went out to bring him in but he too was wounded. The lieutenant in charge of the raid had to be held down to stop him going out to help them. There was no way on earth he could have made it, but that night he did go out and they were brought in. They were both in a terrible state but at least they were alive. All for a loaf of bread.

On our next turn in the line, the Germans kept poking a dummy head above their parapet. They did this all day but we refused to take the bait. The next day they had a helmet on a pole, up and down, up and down. Eventually one of our Lewis gunners lost patience and fired. When he stopped we clearly heard a German voice shout in English 'stop it, stop it'. Then up came the pole again and the same voice cried out 'have another go'!

To complete a most unusual stay, on our last night we were on the receiving end of a heavy shelling in retaliation for a raid by the next-door battalion. Oh what a relief to get away from there!!

Even all that already seems distant. I wonder how clear our recollections will be when it is all over and we are reminiscing as old men over a long luncheon on a quiet Sunday afternoon with the grandchildren banished to the outdoors and the women to the drawing room to provide us with peace and quiet!

I do not know how long we will be here for, a while I do hope as it is an excellent spot. What a joy to be warm, clean and well fed – my needs are no more demanding than a child's at the moment!

Look after yourself, Norman, the firm demands it!

Warmest regards,

Your friend,

WH

★ ★ ★

February 28, 1917
War Office, London

The Military Secretary presents his compliments to Mrs Anderson and begs to inform her that the following report has just been received dated February 27.

Major WH Anderson, Highland Light Infantry, was admitted to General Hospital Dames Camiess with slight pyrexia. Further reports will be sent if received.

★ ★ ★

Diary of Nora Anderson, April 2, 1917
Strathairly

My sons are home. It may not be the end but it is all I would or could want for at this moment. They are home, life and limb intact, the horrors of Flanders Fields left behind. The suffering continues apace and I see it and hear of it all the time. In the village Mrs Somebody will ask if you heard the terrible news about Mrs Someonelse's son or husband, Willie will remark from the newspaper that young Captain Soandso has gone, or Lily will tell me, or Teddie write it. How will any survive?

Yet I am at peace now, altho' it's true I feel myself flood with guilt as I write that. If anyone should read this, especially Willie, well, it would not be a good thing, not at all. Truth be told, it is an enormous comfort, even if I do not look back at what I have written. I confided as much to Jean and she smiled ever so sweetly at me. She told me she rarely reads hers either and that if Ian did stumble across it she would be for the high jump. Then she laughed again in that carefree way of hers, but now the note is different. She has aged of late. She always had a freshness but I cannot see it at the moment. I wonder what she sees when she looks at me? Does one feel old? Does the mind age with the body? I feel the cold so much more than I ever did and this horrid winter has not helped at all. I have felt myself slowing since summer's end last year.

Yet for the last few days, rather it is weeks now, that has changed and I have felt at ease. I have not breathed a word of it to a soul, not Jean or dear Lily. That would not do at all. At moments I dearly would like to say to somebody close that I am at ease again and how that so lightens one's life and even heightens the senses. It certainly feels warmer and I expect that's the worst of the winter past. I have been feeling more active and have started walking Lad again, much to Lily's relief I feel, altho' I most certainly will not take the gun as she implores me to.

I fear I am rambling on today, but it is only because sometimes the mood catches me and I scribble furiously like some inspired playwright. This has become my favourite time, lunch done, Strathairly at ease. I think of it as the house at rest. Willie is in his study catching up on a speech he has to give tonight in Edinburgh. He will leave in about an hour but for now, he is with me and my boys are out of danger. The birds are singing again, I can hear them outside the window in the oak tree. Even the old tree looks a little brighter. I think it is relieved that winter's fearsome grip is beginning to be loosened.

We really have had such snow, which somehow can seem wonderful when there are children about but otherwise becomes only wearisome. I can hear Lily whistling a people's tune somewhere in the house, usually I do not care for whistling by women, yet this afternoon I find it soothing. She is a comfort to me, although I know she longs to have McCullum home. He is, according to her accounts, practically running the farm. Old Mr Ross is not in the first flush, while both of his remaining sons have been called up. Lily said the younger one was

123

desperately keen to take his papers and had twice been refused on account of his being a landworker. Finally, he convinced them that his poor invalid father and McCullum, who is no sort of youngster (Lily says his back will play up after a long day in the fields), were able enough to take care of things themselves. Having managed that he was then furious to be sent to India, where, the last we heard, he remains. That must be some comfort to his father, especially with the older boy with the Gordons in France.

Am I not so blessed with fortune to have mine home?

Of course, both are outwardly chomping at the bit to get out again, altho' I suspect dear Bertie is less so than Ted. I suspect Bertie says he is anxious to go out again as it is what he believes he should say. Dear Bertie, that is so like him, to do as he should. I do not know how long he will be here. He says he hopes for a battalion, and is writing letters to everyone to ensure it will be an HLI one. For now, he is here tho', and that is what matters. He is a good husband and father and his place is here with them. It is, I am sure, where he wants to be. While Teddie, my darling Teddie, so noble and handsome, cares not one jot for those about him (that is why we must care so for Him). He wants his adventure and longs to cross the Channel once more.

They think ever so highly of him down in Kent and Bertie told me (for he dotes on his younger brother and thinks that nobody notices) that is likely to keep him in England for some time to come. They cannot afford to risk losing all their experienced airmen as they are needed to pass on their great knowledge.

Bertie looked so much better this weekend and Gertie too looked much improved and was certainly calmer for having her husband at her side. Even the boys appeared to have grown more with their tall father to look over them once more and their behaviour was impeccable this visit. I do not fool myself that I will see him or Ted much (tho' Bertie did think the chances of them wangling a long weekend visit to Strathairly if he is not sent back soon are good), but it is enough, more than enough if I am to be truthful, to know they are, thank dear God Almighty, out of harm's way.

Ah! Ted may be out of the Germans's way but there is another who has Him in her sights. Gertie told me that Tuppie had asked to go down to London to visit Teddie and Jessie Gilmour was having none of it. Gertie said she had sided with her mother against her sister and that her sister has barely said a word to her since. I too side with Jessie, it is really not the right thing to do at all. The young are so impatient.

Teddie was furious over this decision by our Government that officers must not be seen dining in London after 10 of a night. Quite why they would want to be dining at that time in the first place escapes me. It is not at all helpful for one's health. The young do insist on doing things differently, and the war only seems to quicken their demands and ignorance of how things should be done, tho' I daresay their children will be the same. Any child of Ted's I would expect to be quite a handful if she (I am sure it shall be a she) is to take after her father and young Tuppie. What rows they shall have in their house! I wonder where they shall settle? I have little idea where Teddie's ambitions lie, but it will certainly not be with the firm as he has no head for figures whatsoever. Something in Edinburgh I think would be ideal, then my grandchildren would not be distant. I wonder, shall they look like my knight? His offspring shall be beautiful to behold – I hope I shall not be too old to lift them.

Willie is a different man with the boys back home. He smiles now. Yet it has not stopped him from working ever, ever harder. He says that the war is at a vital stage and we must stand firm until the Americans can send their men to France. He was most occupied with the news from Russia, but dismissed the claims of one of Bertie's friends at dinner on Saturday evening that the same could happen here, springing even from Glasgow. Captain McKimmie asserted that the shipworkers and such in Glasgow would follow the Russian example at the drop of a hat. He said their willingness to strike showed just that. Willie became quite angry, he does so adore Glasgow and its men. Bertie smoothed things over, but he told me later that the argument had flared again over coffee and I do not think Willie cared much for Captain McKimmie.

On the day that we had to wind our clocks forward, Willie had a splendid day with the Red Cross and they raised a large collection. I worry what it takes from him tho', he was ever so tired afterwards. He does not speak much to me of his tiredness, he has never been one to put himself first but I can see.

Sometimes I feel removed from my men. I know Bertie has written to Willie of his experiences at The Front in great detail, yet I know little of it. I tried to speak to him of it while he was at Strathairly, and he would not say a word. They believe that they are protecting me. Yet its affect is instead to set me worrying what horrors are these that they cannot speak or write of them in front of me. That does not help ease my mind one instance.

I should not worry for now tho'. I look at my boys and they are well. Bertie did look ever so pale when he first returned home after his illness. When we visited him in the hospital I was glad Willie had taken me to the station to see that Wounded Train as there were some dreadful sights. This is what puzzles me and, at times, can exasperate. I have seen that horror and I have seen, or rather experienced hurt and still they try to hide from me. What damage could it do?

I should not write like this anymore. This time I have read through this entry and I should be happy, or at least content in these horrid times, that my two boys have found a way home. We are healing. Lord God, have mercy upon us poor souls.

CHAPTER 12

THE LAST WEEKEND

Diary of Nora Anderson, May 21, 1917
Strathairly

We had it confirmed today and they shall both be here this weekend. Oh, it is so close. Teddie's will be just a flying visit. His commanding officer has allowed him to deliver an aeroplane to somewhere near Edinburgh (dear Ted would not tell me where as he says it is terribly secret) and then he shall dash over to Strathairly for a long weekend. Oh, the joy!!

He will have all his flying costume with him and I am going to have more pictures taken to complete my album for the time being. I will have one of him in full costume, his new specially warm coat, hat, gloves and goggles and others of him in his uniform. He looks ever so dashing in his Royal Flying Corps outfit, every inch the Knight of the Air, saviour of us all. I shall have one of Bertie too in uniform, with his Glengarry, and I think family shots as well. We shall be a family once more.

Willie arrived back from London last night. He was tired but surprised me with his talkativeness. All through dinner he chatted away about the service – he does so enjoy his Red Cross work, and, by all accounts (not his own!) prospers at it too. Westminster Cathedral was full to bursting. He read out the newspaper report of the event that he had brought from London, adding his asides as he went. Queen Alexandra, The Princess Royal and even the King and Queen of Portugal (two curious wee people, said Willie) were there. The Prime Minister was to have attended but withdrew. Willie said it was because he was concerned over the reception he might receive from all the wounded men (who made up the mass of the congregation, along with nurses). He says there is dissatisfaction amongst the men, especially those back home nursing wounds who only have the prospect of a return to France to look forward to once they are better. Willie frowns upon such thoughts. We all have to do our duties in every way we can, he says, no matter how horrid, taxing or dreadful those may be.

He did not even like me laughing about the 'Cake Law'. It does seem silly to ban the baking of cakes, but Willie says there is no time for such frivolity and we must conserve all our food for basic sustenance. It is a pity tho' that Lily and I cannot bake one of our special cakes for the boys' return.

How we are going to get enough to feed Teddie I do not know. He eats by the cartload. We have plenty of vegetables as the garden is in full production. He will want Home cooking, but it will be rather different than what he was used to. He will have to eat soup this time – or starve, poor boy! Lily has promised to fetch a rabbit from McCullum on Friday and that will do for Saturday's dinner and she hopes to have a chicken from Ross Farm as well and that would be just the thing for lunch on Sunday. Otherwise it's potato and vegetable stew for all. I have really grown quite fond of it, but I fear it would not be to the boys's taste and it is certainly not to Willie's.

Willie said that he saw some American officers while in London and is of the opinion that it will not be long before they have an army ready for France. That should be just the lift we need to finish this terrible war. With the Americans alongside us and the French there will be no stopping us. Willie spoke with such terrific fervour, at least judged by the standards in which he normally delivers his orations, that I was soon convinced.

I awoke this morning feeling lighter of heart than I have done for a long while. Is there an end in sight? There have been moments today, as I planned the weekend with Lily and helped her make up all the beds, when I really thought I could see it.

This is the fourth year of all this. I do not think about the years gone by. I prefer to look ahead and it cannot, surely not, go on and on. The people cannot take it (regard the poor Russians) and with the Americans now so close, Oh! I can see it. I do think I can see the end. A way home for one and all.

I have not experienced this since it all began. I think it is a mother's sense. I have never dared entertain such thoughts, yet I cannot help myself. Should I dare to allow such thoughts? Oh, what harm can they do. I shall not breathe a word of them to a soul – not a soul. They shall be mine, and if they are to be foolish, well, only I shall know and no harm will have been done to anybody.

I must be allowed to have my mind. One cannot deliver one's entire self to the cause of the moment. It does sound selfish at first, yet one would be wasting the self if there was nothing left for the self. One must feed the self something, some morsel however wee, to keep the self alive.

I am not sure that makes an ounce of sense. My, sometimes I do not know what I write, it just comes out, flowing from I do not know where. It does me good.

Yet for all that there can still be no denying (even amid my merry mood today) the seriousness of our terrible situation. There is still much to do of course, but my spirits will hold back the tiredness. I should not have spent so long writing this.

Lily is still in the kitchen chopping up vegetables. These are not for us now, but for tomorrow's soup kitchen. I am helping her tomorrow and I should be helping her now, but she indulges me, and anyhow I think she is nearly as excited as I about this weekend. She has always been extra fond of Ted and will do anything to make sure he is fed to his satisfaction, or rather her satisfaction, which would be a challenge for any man. I fear Ted may not be able to make his craft airbourne again!

★ ★ ★

Teddie, June 19, 1917
Wiltshire

Dear Bertie,

How fortunate it was to have that leave together. I am sure it will be a long time now before we have such luck again so your golf will be even rustier! I think you really have to work on your back swing and just concentrate that wee bit more.

I thought it was a fine weekend – didn't Mother seem well? It is an age since I have seen her in such fine spirit. And I have not eaten so much, and so well, for an absolute age. I am still full up now! Where do they find that meat? – and it was made even finer by seeing you back on your feet again. Where next for you? Do you think you might get a command yet? Or would you rather go back to the East Surreys? I hope this gets to you before you go, tho' I'm sure Gertrude will send it on if I've missed you.

It is official now, I am a captain – so I am only one behind you! I am to be a flight commander here, altho' they might send me to take over the flight at Lydd. I asked Col Chamier about going back to France and he said I was doing useful work at the moment. I like it here, the work is interesting, but I do want to go back. We also talked about applying for a permanent commission for me. He is keen I do so and I think I will do so. I do enjoy flying, it is great fun, and he said that when the war is over the corps is going to get bigger and bigger (as well as the machines themselves) and go into all sorts of different areas. There will be plenty of opportunity and I am very tempted.

The wonderful thing about being here is that I do get to try out a number of different machines, which is great fun and helps my flying enormously as they are all so different. Some can twist and turn like a kite, whilst others need a strong touch and firm discipline! I go up when I can, most times to instruct but on my own when I get the chance.

Much of what I have to do is instruction but I am also able to try out new ideas that need testing for working with the guns or doing contact patrols. I find it difficult to judge how worthwhile some of these innovations are without being fired at, but I suppose that is rather like the man, you don't know how they will react until they come under fire. We could have the best pilot in England here under our instruction but if they turn out to be gun shy when they get out to France then they are no good to anyone.

I am sure it will amuse you to know that I spend a deal of my day teaching in a classroom! I have to lecture on all matters of aviation and working for corps. It can be frightfully dull and I sometimes lose my place! Now that the weather is better we spend as little time as possible in the classroom and as much as we can in the air, which is a great relief I can tell you.

I was down at Lydd a couple of days ago, where the Kite Balloon Squadron is based and got the chance to go up in one of their balloons. After flying it is such a peaceful experience and you become positively dreamy up there as you look over the green of the English countryside. It is not a job tho' I would care for in France. I think you would feel very exposed and helpless if you saw a Hun machine approaching and I certainly do not fancy hurling myself into the air with only a parachute to see me to the ground. Remember that balloon attack I took part in before the Somme battle? I would not care to be on the wrong end of that. Yet on a summer's afternoon above the garden of England it was a most enjoyable experience!

I also went to the RFC sports day that was held at Ascot. That was another fine day and I saw some familiar faces. Churchill was presenting the cups and prizes. You know he is quite a small man in size.

I have seen two names in the lists recently. I don't think you knew Evan Wilson, he was another Fettes boy and another Argyll. Graham Johnston has also gone, we were at Cargilfield together. He was in the Seaforths. We were friends at school as he was in the same dorm. I have written to his mother.

Write to me soon, altho' I am sure Gertrude will let me know where you are and with which regiment. It doesn't seem right to have my older brother out in France whilst I am back here in England.

With love from,

Teddie

ps Did you ask Gertrude what I asked you to about Tuppie? Let me know what she said as soon as you can.

★ ★ ★

Bertie, July 17, 1917
France

My Darling,

'To love is for the soul to choose a companion, and travel with it along the perilous defiles and winding ways of life; mutually sustaining when the path is terrible with dangers, mutually exhorting when it is rugged with objections, and mutually rejoicing when rich broad plains and sunny slopes make the journey a delight, showing in the quiet distance the resting place we all seek in this world.' GH Lewes

We have now been married for eight years! Does that seem a long time to you? I know it might have through this last year, but this will not last forever and then we will all be together again forever.

Dear Gertie, you are a wonder and you are the purpose of my life. I cannot help but think often of you and the boys back there in Scotland. In truth I try not to as it is easiest to get on with things out here rather than let one's mind linger, but easier said than done!

I have now taken over as second-in-command and I am ever so glad to be back with the HLI. Even tho' it is my first time with this battalion there are some familiar faces and one has undoubtedly been accepted more readily.

Amongst the men it feels strangely reassuring to hear the voices of home all around. When I arrived they were in the line and I did not meet with them till they came out. Since then we have been in reasonably comfortable billets back in reserve – it is less of a shock to the system to be broken gradually back in to France! Should I have had to go straight into the line, as I did last time, then it would have been quite a shock to the old man. Altho' I suppose like swimming at school in that freezing cold baths, it may have been better just to jump straight in! Anyhow we are in the area that has featured prominently in the papers and it is an absolute mess, even back here.

They say Verdun is worse – that is not a place I would care to see then as this is like nothing I have seen before. Where I was with the Surreys bears no comparison and I have not even been up to the line yet. The battalion had 11 days in the trenches and that is why we are being given a decent break now.

On France Day, battalion HQ invited our counterparts from a neighbouring French unit for luncheon and at last I had an opportunity to speak French! I don't think I mentioned that I stayed in Boulogne on the way out and there was not a Frenchman to be seen. I stayed at the Hotel de Bourgoyne, where I often used to stay on the way down to Tours. Local tradition has it that Thackeray used to frequent the place. As for our French Day, well our guests arrived laden down with vin rouge – an acquired taste I can tell you – and I had a terrific time, altho' I'm not all together sure about the others as conversation was somewhat stilted to begin with as no-one else could manage any more than the clumsiest schoolboy French (a damning of the Scottish education system!) so they just smiled at each other and attacked the vin. After a time they spoke to each other loudly with much gesturing and use of empty bottles and cutlery to illustrate their grand schemes to end the war!

I spoke with my equivalent, a small, immaculately turned out Major, who was a lawyer in Toulouse before the war. He was telling me of the mutinous troubles they have had in the French army over the last few months. It seems as if it was quite well spread, but they have done a marvellous job in keeping a lid on it.

I assured him nothing of that sort could happen in our army, certainly not in my experience of the battalions I have served with. He shrugged in a way that reminded me so much of talking with my friends in Tours. I suppose they will be in the army as well, and some are sure to have been in Verdun.

My Major had been there – this is why his unit are now here, for a rest. He said he did not want to dwell on it on what was supposed to be a day of celebration and I did not like to press him. He has given me his address and implored us to go to visit them after the war. He has a wife and two wee children as well, altho' they are a little older than ours.

We left the youngsters to it after that; by then the language barrier had been trampled into the dust and the French were attempting to teach their hosts the words to La Marseillaise!

The camp here is incredibly dusty and the progress of the road that leads to the front is easily followed by the clouds of dust put up by the endless men and countless wagonloads of equipment wending their weary way across a featureless landscape. They say one drop of rain and the whole lot will turn to a gigantic quagmire. For the moment tho' we are comfortable enough and that is all one can ask.

Take care, my love and do not worry, I am sure our ninth year of marriage will be a good one.

Your ever loving husband,

B

★ ★ ★

July 28, 1917
War Office, London

The Military Secretary presents his compliments to Mrs Anderson and begs to inform her that the following report has just been received dated July 27.

Captain EK Anderson, Highland Light Infantry att Royal Flying Corps, was admitted to Manor House Hospital, Folkestone with burns to arms and face. Further reports will be sent if received

★ ★ ★

Diary of Nora Anderson, July 30, 1917
Strathairly

Dear God, I pray that you will heal him.

★ ★ ★

Bertie, August 5, 1917
France

Dear Mr & Mrs Maclean,

It is with much sadness that I write to you about your son, William. You will have received the dreadful news through official communications, but I wanted to write on behalf of the battalion to express our sorrow at his loss and our appreciation for his service to King, country and the comrades of his battalion.

It may offer a small measure of comfort to you to know that William died bravely and quickly. I have spoken to his company commander and to the men and they were full of praise for your son. It would have made you proud to hear them speak of him. He was a good soldier and a good friend to them and always a cheery presence in the trenches. He will be sorely missed by the 12th.

On behalf of the battalion may I offer our condolences at your terrible loss.

Please write to me if you have any questions or are in need of any assistance regarding William.

With all sympathy,
Maj WH Anderson,
Second-in-command, 12th HLI

★ ★ ★

Teddie, August 9, 1917
Kent

Dear Bertie,

I wonder if you heard from Mother or Gertrude, but I have made a terrible fool of myself! It was all dreadfully unfortunate but after spending months trying to avoid getting blown to smithereens by the Hun I nearly managed to do it to myself. How embarrassing! And in front of all my trainees too!!

It was rather painful. I was taking a class of observers, teaching them about artillery observation at the airfield at Lydd and was instructing them about fuses, powder puffs and such forth. I set a fuse for 10 seconds but it was faulty and as I made to throw it, the thing went off in my hand. There was this enormous bang, everybody flung themselves to the floor and I was left standing there, sheathed in smoke and ears ringing like thunder. To begin with I think I must have been in shock as I felt nothing, just numb. Then when I realised I was hurt, the pain began and it was actually jolly sore.

They took me to Manor House hospital in Folkestone, where they treated wounds to my right arm and face and packed me off to bed. I had a couple of wobbly days but then it just became frustrating sitting around doing nothing so I badgered them to let me back here – there is plenty I can still do, and I will be flying again soon enough too – and they let me go two days ago and so I'm now back at war with a suitable scar to match! I wonder if I shall get a wound stripe!

In the hospital I did have time to read all the papers every day and I have seen the terribly long lists. I have seen many HLI names so it appears as if you've been in the thick of it. I don't like to read the lists, but you sometimes can't help yourself. I stopped looking at them last month as I had seen so many familiar names. It is not only the names of old friends from schooldays or home, but also the number of pilots who had come through here. It seemed as if they were being trained for the blink of an eye and then off to France and then on to the pages in the papers. And in those few lines of an obituary you learnt more about them than you did in the few brief weeks they were under your command. It does nothing for one's morale.

Sometimes I feel very old and I feel guilty sometimes as well. I think I would be serving better back in France and I think I shall make moves soon to try to return. Surely as an experienced pilot, experienced in battle, I should be more use as a flight commander in France than here in Kent? You are out there doing your bit in amidst it all, whilst I sit here out of harm's way.

One benefit from being back here (when I've not been trying to blow myself up!) is that I have definitely become a better pilot. I have a much greater control of the machine now and of many sorts of machines as well.

I have also decided to apply for a permanent commission. You see this is what I love doing so much, flying really is for me. The RFC is only going to become larger and larger and there will be so many opportunities for those like me. And I am only young! Cloudland is where I belong and where I want to stay. One day I would like to fly all around the world – circumnavigate the world in my own machine. You could come with me as my navigator and observer. We could fly to Rhodesia and see where Ronnie lived and then India to where Charlie was stationed and then on round, all the way to Australia and back around the other side.

Do you think I am being foolish – it's only one of Little Ben's schemes will you say? But, Bertie, I am good at flying and I think it is the best thing for me.

I know you are terribly busy, but when it quietens down with you do write and tell all your news. You know on some days people here on the south coast swear they can hear the guns. I have always been sceptical of that, but on the morning the attack on Ypres began one of our mess sergeants said he thought he could hear a distant rumble, so perhaps it is true after all. •

Love from,
Teddie

★ ★ ★

Bertie, August 31, 1917
France

Dear Mr & Mrs Thomson,

On behalf of the battalion I would like to express our sympathy on the recent loss of your son, Albert. As you may have read in the newspaper we have been involved in a series of big pushes on the enemy and Albert played his part in them to the full until the very end. It may be of some consolation to you to know that your son died bravely and quickly.

He was a credit to you, King, country and the comrades of his battalion.

I have spoken to his company commander and the men who served with him and they all miss him terribly. They said he was always a cheery presence in the trenches as well as a fine soldier. I wish you could have heard them speak of your son. We were all proud to have served with him.

At this dreadful time, our thoughts are with you. The 12th is poorer without him.

Please write to me if you have any questions or are in need of any assistance regarding Albert.

In deepest sympathy,
Maj WH Anderson
Second-in-command, 12th HLI

★ ★ ★

Bertie, September 4, 1917
Flanders

Dearest Mother & Dad,

Well, what a time of it we have had. I must apologise for not writing for so long but we have been in it up to our necks. I am sure Gertrude will have passed on what little news I managed to send to her. I am well, in good health actually, altho', like everyone, very tired.

We are out of the line now and set for a spell in reserve to catch our breath, rest and build up our strength again. It is very welcome indeed.

The battalion has suffered in the last month or so, but we have still been fortunate compared to many others. I heard that the East Surreys caught it again and lost Colonel de la Fontaine. They really have had wretched luck.

We have been ever so busy really since the end of July and in some awful conditions as well. It has been as bad as at any time last winter. Yet we have come through and I feel we are a stronger battalion for it.

It has been an experience of the like I could never have imagined and one that I do feel in a way privileged to have had. It can only strengthen one as a man. I have been fortunate to witness the bravery of man and comradeship of an extraordinary people under such extremes

137

that cannot have ever been foreseen. Whilst I have witnessed the horrors, and it is not something I would desire to face again (but I am prepared to do so), I have also seen the noble side of man, the humanity of man, and have been blessed to do so.

Men of all ages and backgrounds, miners from Ayrshire, merchants from Glasgow and crofters from Argyll, coming together, united in the cause of good, loyal to each other, building comradeships that will never be broken, not even in death. Their good cheer, relentless enthusiasm and, above all, unswerving, understated courage has been a joy to behold. There is tragedy all around. We have witnessed it every day, but one really cannot allow oneself to dwell on such as then it would be impossible to lead and perhaps even impossible to survive.

There is a Persian proverb that I wrote down long ago that could best describe the spirit that permeates this battalion:

'Help thou thy brothers' boat across and lo! thine own has touched the shore.'

You know life in the trenches is not all horrors tho'. Even in the last month or so there have been moments of peace and moments of surprise when one forgets where one is, the occasional sight that raises a smile or promotes an air of contentment for just a brief spell. These moments play a large part in keeping one going. I had one in particular just a few days ago as we were coming towards the end of our time in the line. We did not get much of a summer over the last couple of months, but in those last few days, as quiet returned to the battlefield, the sun came out. One day as I was making my tour of the forward trench, I paused with my servant to have a moment in the sun and a peaceful cigarette, a moment of calm. We were leaning on the back of the trench, our faces turned gratefully towards the warming sun, when all of a sudden there was a whirr-whirr from in front of the trench, in no-man's land, and a pair of partridge swept past. It would not have felt right to have a pot, even tho' they would have been a more than welcome addition to the plainness of our diet. It was a wonderful moment, but it gave us quite a fright at first as well!

The bird life can astonish at times. These last few days it has been plentiful, altho' how any of them have survived the barrages of the last few weeks God alone knows. I have twice woken to the sounds of birds, chirruping above the dugout's entrance, which has an extraordinarily calming influence. One sees swallows darting about above the trenches and magpies hop about, always curious. Then comes the return of the more usual sounds of war and they all disappear only to return seemingly by some miracle unscathed when all is peaceful again. Where do they hide? For all these horrors, nature's path cannot be altered it would seem.

I must tell you what I can about our involvement in the battles of the last weeks. I have yet to see any newspapers so do not know what you may already be familiar with, but I am sure you will have established just where I have been.

It is only now when one has stopped that it is possible to consider the events and in all honesty it is difficult to remember clearly exactly what happened and just how one was involved. Once the whole thing starts, it all happens so quickly, time flies by, and by the end of the day one can barely recall how one ended up in that spot.

We were involved in a raid before the attack itself. I had planned it and it went well, in fact Captain Myles, who led it, was awarded the MC, but the poor soul never knew as he fell five days afterwards. He brought back a number of prisoners and the state of the Hun gave us a great boost ahead of the big push. They were in a terrible way and said they had not eaten for two days (their supply lines were ruined as we shelled the enemy trenches for two weeks before the attack itself. The noise! Even we were grateful when it ended).

After the raid we were relieved for a last day of preparation and then we were marched back to the front. We had to make our way up the night before as there is absolutely no cover on our side and the enemy would have spotted us instantly had we made the move by day.

It was a long and tiring night, it is very difficult to find one's way about after dark and we were slipping and sliding in the mud as it had rained the day before, but it did take one's mind off the forthcoming attack. You know I did not have time to feel at all worried about what awaited us as there was so much to be done and it came as a surprise when my servant said we ought to be getting to HQ for the attack itself was shortly to begin. By then the bombardment was at its peak and one had to shout even to be heard by one's neighbour. We made it to battalion HQ shortly before 4am and just as the whistles began to blow. After that I could not be sure what happened.

At first it seemed to go well, but later it became increasingly confusing and the going became rather difficult. We acquitted ourselves well of that I am sure, but the ground was the consistency of porridge and it was very difficult to get anywhere.

The divisions on our flanks were not making as rapid progress and so we became exposed and then had to face the enemy counterattacks. For three days we were in the middle of it and I cannot, and really do not yet want to, give you any sort of description of the events suffice to say we came through somehow.

We of course suffered losses. Alfred Taylor, our medical officer and a fine man, was lost whilst dressing a soldier's wounds on the battlefield. I have written to his wife. He had two children.

We had a brief respite when we were taken out of the line but then it was back up as support for the next large attack on the 22nd. We moved up as dawn broke and the scene was one of devastation and it was extremely hard going. The men become simply weighed down such is the amount they have to carry and find themselves sinking into the mud. The duckboard roads are themselves covered and treacherous, it is very easy to lose one's footing and take an unwanted dirty bath. We got into position and waited to be sent over, but at 10 o'clock it was cancelled and we waited till around lunchtime when we were told to move the battalion forward ready to attack that night. By four o'clock we were in position and waited and waited. I actually found the waiting rather more difficult this time. Then at half past six we were told the attack had been cancelled. One can't help feeling a wave of relief at moments such as that.

The following day we had more of the same and eventually we were moved into the line where the next day we were on the receiving end of the worst shelling I have experienced. It went on for two days and was terribly trying on the nerves, but again it is the men around you who help one pull through.

We had to repel one large enemy counterattack that took some doing and cost us many men but we hung on. Then we were moved to another part of the line where battalion HQ was in a place called Wild Wood, it was indeed wild but only some skeletal tree stumps gave any indication of a wood of any sort. That was to be our last stop and at last we were taken out. I don't think I have ever felt so tired.

I am resuming this later in the day — we have just finished dinner — and reading it through it strikes me that it does not give a very clear description of what went on, but that is how it seemed at the time. To take part in an attack is a dreadful experience but one does feel that it has to be done and it is better to do that than merely sit around here waiting in our holes in the ground.

You must not worry about me – if I can come through that I will come through anything! It is, of course, not the life one would chose, even for your enemy, but I will play my part and willingly and come back to Scotland a better man for it.

Your loving son,
Bertie

★ ★ ★

Mrs Taylor, September 6, 1917
Newcastle-under-Lyme

My dear Major Anderson,

I am moved to thank you for your long letter and considerate thoughts over Alfred's death. Your affection for my poor husband and the experiences you were able to share with me mean a great deal to a grieving widow. With all that you have to address and the vast difficulties of your surroundings, taking the time to think of my husband's family leaves me in your debt.

It is a comfort that Alfred met his end alongside such men as you and the 12th. He always wrote with so much pride of serving in the 12th. Even though he was not a Highlander, nor a Scot he felt so at home with your brave and noble men. Neither was he even a military man before this great war began, but he wanted to serve and put his doctoring to the best possible use.

I would ask for one more letter, and I dearly hope that is not unfair of me, or indeed wrong of me. I have never had the pleasure of meeting you, but Alfred wrote of you tenderly and that is why I make this request.

I believe that you cared for Alfred and that showed to me in your kind letter and I wonder whether you might write me once more. I must learn more of his final day. I cannot rest unless I know all about his end. I owe that to him and our children and I implore you to comfort me with that information.

Did the soldier he was tending to on the battlefield when he suffered that mortal blow survive?

If he did, perhaps he could also write me and tell me what my husband said to him and the exact circumstances. If he cannot write, perhaps you could transcribe for him.

Will you please grant me this last request? I humbly beg this of you.

Forgive me my demands, see I knew him so well in life and I have to know his end so well also. I need to know him too in death.

May God bless you and your family and I pray for your safe return to Scotland unscathed by this brutality.

With kindest regards and affection,

Mrs AR Taylor

CHAPTER 13

NOWHERE

Diary of Nora Anderson, September 19, 1917
Lansdowne Crescent, Glasgow

We have had a quiet and mercifully peaceful day today. It has been most welcome as yesterday was ever so busy and I was really quite exhausted last night. I could not even face writing. Tomorrow I hope to return to Strathairly and I am so looking forward to it. I do want to get back there before the weather turns. I hope we do not get another winter like last as I would find that most difficult to cope with.

The last felt endless, an unceasing grip on poor Scotland for week after week, month after long month and I fear for her suffering another battering. I fear our country is weak. These long years have taken their toll. I see it in the street when I return to Glasgow and I see it when I return home again. There are few smiles to be found in Scotland.

There was an attempt at some form of merriment surrounding the King's visit and I did enjoy yesterday for a time. The Ibrox Park was very crowded and everybody cheered when the King entered and drove around the athletic track in front of the stands. But there is no escape from our current situation (and I increasingly do not condemn those who do seek moments of escape, just a moment here and there, even for we who are far from danger. It maintains one's sanity), even as he invested soldiers and workers with medals to mark their achievements.

There was one young soldier, a private, who was carried on to the stage in an invalid chair to receive the Victoria Cross from the King. The King had to bend down to pin it on the young man's breast as he cannot stand. He was younger even than Teddie. He received tremendous cheers and applause, but his weak smile in response tore open what must reside within every mother the world over, and I found it all rather difficult after that. I wanted to get home, away from the crowds and the noise. The jollity felt false and I could see everywhere forced smiles masking deep hurts.

They say that there are families in Glasgow who are struggling to feed their children, I know that there are families at home who have little with which to feed themselves. I heard of one good wife from a village in Fife who near starved herself for a week before her husband returned from the front so there would be ample to put on the table when he came home and he would think they, at least, were well cared for back home whilst he served his country in France.

The news from France continues to raise hopes one day and then deny them the next. This great battle has raged in Flanders for day after day after day and the newspapers are full of the ebb and flow of events and then on the next page a list of the departed that plucks so cruelly from every house in the land. Ypres is not a name that will be held dear by future generations of fatherless Britons. I thank God each evening that my Teddie is still safe in England and then I pray to the Lord that he will bring Bertie home.

Lily informed me only a few days ago that Mrs Lewis told her while queuing at the shop that she would accept her husband coming home without an arm or a leg if only he would come home. I told Lily that we should have no such thoughts like that and she should discourage them if they were raised in her presence again. I did not mention what Lily had said to Willie.

Oh my dear Willie. On he goes. I do fear for him. At times he looks close to exhaustion but he will not be told. He has stayed home today and it has been pleasant to have his quiet company. We have so little of it now.

So we go on. Willie here in Glasgow, working himself to the bone, and I across Scotland at Strathairly, finding means to pass the days. I wonder if I should do more, but I do not feel strong. I have taken to walking Lad again, but we are both aged in recent years and so potter at our own pace, not very far and not very fast. Our pace would drive Ted to distraction. He was never one to standstill or even slow for a moment. His life has to be lived at the gallop.

We are having a good broth tonight, made from vegetables I brought from our ever-growing vegetable garden at Strathairly. It is really Lily's pride and joy and she is sure that she is much better with the soil than McCullum.

Gertie is arriving with the children imminently and I must ready myself. They are growing ever so quickly and I do hope their father does not miss too much more of their early life. That shall be my prayer this night.

★ ★ ★

Bertie, October 12, 1917
Flanders

My darling,

Back in the line again. Thank you for the parcel, what a Godsend that was. I have just shared the last of the cheese with a very grateful adjutant and orderly and am now writing this as everyone settles down to snatch some sleep before dawn.

You know it is nearly three years since Charlie went and two years since Ron, and still we are here. When will this ever end?

Before the battles of August and September I had never witnessed such an amount of men as we massed for those days and I never stopped to think throughout the days that followed. Only now that we are back into the routine of a turn in the front and then a break of sorts behind, does the realisation come of how little has been gained despite such strength.

And if that could not break them what shall? Shall we be sitting here, in this mud and filth for the rest of our lives surrounded by the smell of death amidst an ever-changing cast of brave young men written to play only a brutally fleeting and quickly forgotten role in the history of this enormous conflict?

Shall you and hundreds of thousands of wives and mothers have to sit alone for ever more? My darling, how will my sons know me?

It is the coming of winter that brings this black shroud. You must forgive my melancholia, but this is a cure for it. I dare not talk of these feelings here. It would be neither fair nor right. You are an outlet for me, you help me go on. I try to think of that Arab expression 'the desert is the garden of Allah', but I think one has to be terribly strong to find true comfort in it and I do not know how strong I really am.

I do not think I ever wrote you of the flowers we saw in the summer. Sometimes we would have a small posy of wild flowers on our table in the dugout. And if you could have the seen the poppies, sprayed red across no-man's land.

I am reading the book of Burns you sent me.

'But pleasures are like the poppies spread,
You seize the flow'r; its bloom is shed;
O like the snow falls in the river,
A moment white – then melts for ever.'

I read that this evening – it is the first time I have read Tam O'Shanter for such a long time – and that set me thinking about the summer. That went long ago and now there is nothing but the uniform of mud. Nothing to brighten the spirit.

Oh darling, I am tired and I fear I am getting more windy. When I first came out I was scared at moments, but they were only moments and quickly passed. Now I have this flickering in my stomach more or less constantly when we are in the line, tho' it is at its worst when we are coming in. I do hope no-one has noticed. Sometimes my hand shakes. One becomes resigned to it. I can cope and I will. We convince ourselves that we will come through but one also accepts that it could happen and if it will it will.

I may not send this, but writing it helps me and I know you would not begrudge me that. Right now it is quiet. I can hear the gentle breathing of the others as they lie in our dark, damp shelter beneath the earth. I do not think they are all sleeping as sleep does not always come easy, especially when it is quiet. It is then the thoughts crowd one's mind, bringing questions that dare not be answered. You know I actually slept during a barrage towards the end of the battle. It was on the first of two days of constant shelling. We were all tired, I had been caught in a shell hole between two posts – the lines here are not well established – when it began and as I pressed myself into the soil I felt my eyes grow heavy and the next thing I knew my servant was shaking me awake. He thought I had been hit, but instead I had slept through half an hour at the height of the bombardment. I will not have a stranger nap in my life.

Thank you for sending the papers. It is strange indeed to read of something one has played a part in and I found it quite impossible to establish exactly what our role was altho' our division gets a glowing mention.

The papers are not popular out here at the moment and I, for one, certainly can find them trying. Everyday it seems they hail a great success, one day it is in Salonika, the next in Italy and another Serbia or with the French, but still we are here for all our and our Allies 'Glorious Successes'. 'Another Great Success' they said of Ypres just the other day, well their glory is in short supply around here and there is little sign of any success either.

All they have got right is to call it the battle of the swamps. We are the swamp people. One is never dry, let alone clean. Keep on, keep on says Lloyd George. Well, for how long? We are sinking into Belgium.

The weather has become worse and the mud is all embracing. I have no doubt there shall be some attached to this letter.

People are really becoming stretched to the limit. This morning the Germans were sniping at some stretcher bearers from the next-door battalion who were labouring through the morass worn down by their wretched load. They had picked off three out of four when all of a sudden this officer leapt from the trench picked up a Red Cross flag and marched across to the German line where he berated them loudly in English then marched back again. They did not take a shot at him and did not snipe again for the remainder of the day.

Teddie tells me he has decided to apply for a permanent commission. He also writes of how he wants to come back out. I have told him he has done his bit and continues to serve an important need at Lydd, but I do not think it will have much affect on him. He says he is recovered from his accident apart from a suitably warlike scar on his face, which no doubt is relished by our knight of the air. Little Ben no more! He was most grateful for the long letter you sent him and I have no doubt he is being bombarded with similar from your sister!

I can hear the rain falling outside again and the puddle in middle of the floor is rising again, but I must make my way out as it is not long now till dawn and we must stand to for another day.

'Love hopeth all things and endureth all things.'

With all my love, B

* * *

Diary of Nora Anderson, November 6, 1917
Strathairly

Gertie left this afternoon for Woodbank and we are to care for the children for a day or two. The Gilmours sent a telegram requesting she come at once as they have received news that Allan has been wounded. The telegram was addressed only to Mrs Anderson so it was I who opened it. I recognised it was not one of the military ones at once, but there have been precious few times during this wretched affair that we have received a telegram bearing any welcome news so I expected only ill-fortune as I opened it there in the hall.

I confess that I had a 'moment' when I saw it was not the coming of further heartbreak for my family. It was a moment of relief I suppose and I do feel ever so guilty about it now. It was a terrible thought to have and I really must not be so selfish.

Gertie was with the children in the play room and I sent Lily to bring her down while she instead amused the boys for a time. Gertie has always been close to her brother, more so than Maggie or Tuppie, but she was very brave when she read the telegram. I handed it to her rather than read from it as I thought that was the kindest way and she made immediate plans to leave for the west. My prayers go with her.

★ ★ ★

Bertie, November 11, 1917
France

My darling,

What news? I saw it in the paper only this morning and then your letter arrived this afternoon. He has always been a strong man and if a man has his strength it is always possible to pull through. I am sure it is better he is out in Salonika as well. The hospitals are less overrun than they are in France and the climate is better too. I know it will have come as a terrible shock, but there is no reason to fear the worst. The doctors are very good and, of course, now well accustomed to treating all war wounds. It will be a long and anxious wait, but you must think for the good. It will take more than a Bulgar to stop one of you Gilmours! Do let me know at once any news.

How is Meg? What a terrible shock it must have been for her. You must be strong for her and for your family.

Here it is starting to turn cold and those gloves you sent me are coming in much use. We came out of the line two days ago and are now billeted in what was an oil factory before the war. There is ample room, but it is on the chilly side! We are set for a run of roughly eight days in the line and eight days out, which is bearable enough altho' the sector we are in remains fevered.

This has the promise of a good few days for the men as we begin football trials for a game against the East Lancs at the end of the week. The men all adore their football and we are having a series of games between companies before the battalion team is chosen. It is occupying the men even more than the promise of baths for everyone over the next couple of days! It is just the thing to lighten the mood after a difficult spell.

Those not interested in the football, and there are not many in this battalion, have a concert party to look forward to in four days time. There is almost a holiday mood and the CO is happy for that to continue for a few days, as long as it does not get out of hand. Sometimes it is good to try and forget where one is, just for a moment.

We had a lively time of it in our last stay in the line. Brigade were always pressing us to carry out raids and then another battalion carried one out from our front so we had to cope with the retaliation, altho' thankfully it was surprisingly light.

Our frontline was named Devil's Trench, a deserving label if ever there was, and the Hun were always keen to add to its reputation. They were a very active lot. The most alarming moment came when a party of around 40 were spotted making for a gap in the wire and we had to let them have a hasty bombing. They replied in kind and it was a tense time until they retired to their own lines. Crawford was wounded by a bomb splinter but will be fine after a spell in hospital. If people are got there quick enough, the doctors these days can save just about anyone.

I will have to stop now as I must put in an appearance at the football. You do not have me to worry about.

Be strong, my darling, and be patient. It will take time, and it may seem like an age, but he can pull through. Have faith.

Your ever loving husband,

B

* * *

December 24, 1917

The Times, London

Captain Allan Gilmour, Yeomanry, attached Cameron Highlanders, only son of Mr & Mrs William Ewing Gilmour of Woodbank, Alexandria, Dumbartonshire, has died of wounds. He was a native of Vale of Leven and was called up with his regiment at the outbreak of the war. He was educated at Edinburgh Academy and Oxford University, and played Rugby for Oxford and Edinburgh Academy. He was a member of Loch Lomond Rowing club and of Bonhill School Board and was in business in Alexandria.

CHAPTER 14

FALL

Diary of Nora Anderson, January 1, 1918
Strathairly

It snowed again last night, the heaviest fall for some days. It creates a pretty picture from my bedroom window, a white veil draped over the garden. There is a single track of footsteps disturbing the surface of the lawn, but otherwise the even whiteness is unbroken, untouched everywhere else by man. It is so quite, so peaceful.

Its effect is restful, it makes one feel warm and snug being in here and looking out on such perfect a scene. It is as a Christmas scene from an old book and I part believe that if I watch for long enough children will burst out from the house and scamper joyfully across the lawn, yelling with delight as they leave their slight imprints while heading for the field, their toboggans tugged behind and their breath clouding the clear air.

That is what it used to be like at my Strathairly. Each Christmas the house would be full and Willie would spend much of the day hidden in his study searching for peace and quiet. In the afternoon the children would hunt for him, swaddled in coats they would run through the garden sounding squeals of delight as they searched under every tree and shrub, every blade of grass even. All the time he would sit in his study and draw hastily on his pipe, knowing that discovery was growing ever closer and when we could keep them outside no longer they would tumble into the house, leaving a pile of hats, coats and boots in the hall, and at last they would burst into the study and Willie would greet them with a beam of delight and then shepherd them down to the kitchen where Lily prepared hot chocolate and cake for all.

I have always looked fondly on Christmas. I have been blessed to have such happy memories that I will always hold dear.

Willie and I did our best this time, but when it is just the two of us at a time like this it can be very hard. I wrote yesterday to Jean and that made me think at least I am fortunate enough to have my husband alongside me. I will not lose him to this war.

The newspapers said that plum pudding was served in the trenches on Christmas Day.

Four Christmases now this has gone on. And always the same. The spring nurtures optimism, summer brings it into bloom, late summer there is the bloody harvest of our young men and by autumn the country is sinking into a morass of despair, bare fields and bare homes. Then Christmas and the seed is planted again that by the next time all will be done. I pray this year will be different.

Bertie, thank God, is safe again from today. He is due to land in England later and will be back in Scotland tomorrow as long as the night train runs as it should. He is going straight to Woodbank and then I think means to see Gertie home to Glasgow. She has been at Woodbank ever since the terrible news, as I do not think she cannot stand to be on her own. Then they will come over here for a time. I do not know how long they will stay, but he has been blessed with a good long leave and as long as he and Teddie are away from France I am content.

When he does come I intend to have a birthday celebration for him. I have knitted him a pair of especially thick socks and Lily has promised to bake a cake (just this once) and will scour the village to make sure she has everything she needs. He did used to so enjoy Lily's cakes and even though he may be 36 he still has a sweet tooth and I know he won't be able to resist it!

I wonder what he will make of this country now. We are a subdued lot I fear, although everybody does make an extra effort when the men come home. The Prime Minister said in his Christmas message that we must hang on until the Americans start arriving in numbers and I fear that is all we are doing now, hanging on, whether it be the wretched men at the front or we families back home.

I finished my album this morning. It looks splendid. Teddie's pictures have turned out ever so well and he looks every inch the dashing Knight of the Air. I am very pleased with the ones of he and Bertie together at Strathairly last summer, both in uniform and Ted looks just as grown up as his older brother. I hope they shall be together again soon.

I shall carry it with me wherever I go.

Teddie, February 11, 1918
Hursley Camp, Winchester

Dearest Bertie,

It was so good to see you on your way through. What a shame we did not know about your promotion then, for we could have given it a suitable welcome! What a start to the year, you get a battalion and Dad gets a CBE – quite a family! I am hopeful that this will be the year that I get a squadron as well. Would you know if Dad will come down to London to receive it? If he does I should be able to get up to town for a time at least. It would be tremendous if Mother came as well. Can you imagine Dad and Mother going to the palace!!

I could then take them out to dinner as I know places where you can still get a good meal despite all this rationing talk. There's one reason for going back to France (for the RFC at any rate – not sure you men of foot feel the same way), the food we had over there was much more interesting than the drab fare we are served here.

I have had another long talk with Col Chamier – it was he who recommended me for a permanent commission – and now he is putting me forward for a squadron! He said he was very pleased with what I had done as a Flight Commander and thought I had proved myself ready for a squadron. He actually put me forward last year, but I haven't been 'approved' yet. If – he says when – I do get a command it will mean I will almost certainly return to France. How strange it would seem for me to be in charge of a squadron!

What did you make of Chamier? He is quite intense but a fine commanding officer I think. He studies everything with the utmost care and is a fine flyer as well. He was on the Somme at the same time as I was – and long before – in charge of 34 Squadron. He is not just an office man, as some of these home based COs can be, and still likes to get up as much as possible. He was one of the first to come up with the idea for getting out of a spin: first you switch off your motor, you make sure your control stick is in the middle and pushed forward and you have your rudder positioned in the centre. I tell you, you need a cool head to establish that works whilst plunging earthwards!

It was a terrible shame the weather was so awful while you were here as I would have so enjoyed taking you up and I am sure it would have thrilled you as well.

The weather here has continued poor and we have not been up much at all since Christmas, tho' it seems nothing to what you've been having up there. I wonder if you managed to get to Woodbank when Loch Lomond froze. What a sight that must have been. I have never seen it frozen. The papers said that the loch steamer was frozen in at Balloch Pier and that men were able to curl at Balloch as well so thick was the ice. And snowstorms in Glasgow!

It is cold down here and when we do go up I don't think I have ever felt so chilled. Perhaps in France as there is so much more to concentrate on, you do not feel the cold as strongly.

Without much flying the work here can be a little slow, I really am not a classroom man! This year I must go back to France, I have been here long enough and if I do not go back soon I worry that I will have forgotten the tricks to taking on the Hun and living with Archie.

Have you seen much of Tuppie? I have not heard from her for a time and I have been writing to her. If you see her do give her a prompt!

If you have the chance do drop in on your way out, or I could come up to London and meet you off the train if you were able to let me know the day. I am sure Col. Chamier would not mind me popping up to town to see you off. I could come up after the morning flight.

If I am not able to meet you, do have the best of luck with the command. I am very proud of my old brother!

With love from,
Teddie

★ ★ ★

Bertie, March 9, 1918
France

My darling G,

Well, this is the 12th day of my command and so far so good! And I am soon to be officially an acting Lieutenant Colonel as I have been advised that will come through any day now.

It has all been quite straightforward. To take command of a battalion with which one is not familiar would be so much more difficult, instead here I know all the faces and have been part of the battalion through some trying times. I already have an idea of who is good at what and which man best suited to certain tasks. I am very happy with my HQ, they are a fine staff.

Of course, in the companies there are officers I do not know as they have arrived during my time at home but I mean to make an effort to get out as much as possible and get myself seen. It does mean so much to me to command an HLI battalion. Better than Norman and his Camerons!

I am writing this on a train – I hope to finish it before we reach our destination as we are not making very rapid progress. It has just gone midnight and we came out of the line tonight after a brief but testing time. There is much tension around as it seems certain the German attack, long predicted by everyone, is now imminent. The lot opposite were certainly very jumpy over the last couple of days. Battalion HQ was in this strong point in the line, one taken from the enemy at such cost last year. It was one of those that made their line so formidable but now it has to face the other way and we have reinforced it as much as possible. It was quite crowded in there, which made it rather uncomfortable but at least brought a degree of warmth, which everyone here was most thankful for.

I was really very fortunate to be out of the last couple of months as they say it was extremely cold, the worst they have had to put up with and that made the line even more miserable. It made me feel somewhat guilty I have to say, but then no-one seems to begrudge anyone their leave – especially not an old man like me!

Anyhow, this point had around 30 men defending it as well as all my HQ staff and the enemy took a liking to us all. We came into the line in the afternoon and I was given a warm welcome to my first command at the front by a night of heavy shelling. Whether it was because I felt I had to try and set an example or not, or whether it was just the benefit of a good rest I do not begin to know, but I felt more at ease under this fire than certainly I had back in December, much less shaky.

Nevertheless they gave us a good going over that night and the next day was just as hot. They continued to shell us almost continually and, for good measure, gave us regular bursts of machine-gun fire. It made for a hairy tour of our positions and we were grateful to get back to HQ unscathed.

We spent that night building up the wire to our front. If you could see it; it is an impenetrable forest of jagged edges which should prove a weighty barrier to any attack. That same evening they did mount an attack further north and we could hear sounds of a furious battle for most of the night.

I presume it met with little success as we were issued with no further orders that night or the following morning. That day, actually to-day but it already seems so long ago, was even worse. The shelling increased and they also hurled gas shells at us so it has been a thoroughly uncomfortable time but thankfully through it all our casualties have been mercifully light.

There can really be no doubt that an attack is on the way. It is really only a question of where it comes and when. It will be a tremendous test for us all, certainly the greatest I have faced but I feel ready for it with these men around me. They have all made it so easy to take over and I do not feel a desperate need to have to prove myself worthy of the command. That examination will soon have to be sat whether I like it or not and so there is little point in attempting some grand gesture in the meantime.

For all I am relishing the chance to command, when this is all over I will not be following Little Ben. I am too old for a start! I will be done with my soldiering and it will be you, the boys and the firm for me. I wonder whether Teddie would think differently had he a family. I wonder when he will have a family! Sooner than we think? He told me about the brooch for Tuppie. Of course, he still has years on his side. It does raise a smile to think of him as really just a boy at the start of all this and now soon he will be leading a squadron in the Flying Corps. He is proving to be quite the military man; and at such a young age. There are times when you cannot imagine that he only turned 21 last summer; as there are also times when you are reminded that he is still ever so early in his life. I hope it is a mix that will benefit him when this is all over; it is not good to lose that youthfulness, with all its enthusiasm and dash, at too young an age.

This train is giving me the time to write the longest letter of my life – we have just ground to a halt again. I am not at all sure where we are headed, but I know that we are to be held in camp somewhere to wait on events as some sort of emergency reserve ready to plug any gaps that may appear. At least then we have the chance of being fresh when it all gets underway. I cannot but help have a feeling of excitement over what is approaching. Perhaps it will be the first step towards the end. I feel sure we will stop whatever comes at us, these men will not yield and it will be an inspiration for me to be at their head.

I did not know what to expect coming back after such a time at home. I was anxious, and if I am to be honest fearful. It is the biggest challenge of my life – I shall surely never face a greater one – and it was with reluctance that I crossed London, boarded that miserable train and headed for the coast. The contrast between the train up to London, full of smiling men heading for their homes, and the one making the return journey with its cargo of quiet reflection for one part and forced jollity for the other is something to behold.

I remember Ron writing of the peacefulness of the crossing to France. I stood on deck and listened to the ship's progress – for one could see nothing – and I thought of Ronnie and Charlie and Allan. And I thought of all those other names one has seen in the newspapers in the last four or so years. I know I should not have, but sometimes in a strange way it helps, like taking a deep breath before diving in again. One can be sure of being here.

I then thought of Orme Angus writing:

'To let the dead bury its dead, to live in the present and for the future, is not only a stern duty but the only recipe for a happy life.'

And I decided as I stood on that ship's deck that I shall adopt that as my motto from now until the end.

The end? We all live for the end and we talk sometimes of what we shall do when it comes, but I do not encourage too much of it. Now that is something that has to be rationed! Writing to one's loved ones is the place for such hopes and fears, giving too much voice to them can make men wistful and dreamy, which then becomes a barrier to performing one's duty.

When I write these letters at times like this, not knowing when I will have to end it, I find myself just writing on and on, laying out my jumbled thoughts as they come straight from my mind. I hope they make some sort of sense! For as I have often written they are an outlet, both in detailing our experiences and those feelings and emotions that are otherwise best stored, especially so when in command. I do so savour writing them, as well as receiving the replies. I keep them all you know. I look forward to the moments when I can settle in a corner with my pencil and begin to scribble, even more so as those chances appear to be less and less frequent whilst in command.

We are moving again and John Cox has just come in to inform me we are close to our destination so I will have to stop. I will post it here, wherever here might be, so you will have it soon.

Do not worry, my darling, I am fine and prospering back here in France.

Your ever loving husband, B

★ ★ ★

March 19, 1918
The Times, London

News in brief
Flying Accident
An aeroplane crashed at Worthy Down, near Winchester on Saturday. The pilot, Captain EK Anderson, attached to the Royal Flying Corps from the Highland Light Infantry, later died of his wounds.

★ ★ ★

Matron Helena Appleton, March 20, 1918
The Royal Hampshire Hospital, Winchester

Dear Mrs Anderson,

I was the Matron caring for your boy when he came to our hospital and I wanted to write you to express my deepest sympathy over your terrible loss.

He was in a very bad way when he arrived with us, yet to the very end he was an officer and thinking of others even in his state and at such a tender age. He came in on the 16th and passed peacefully away the following day

I was with your boy nearly all the time and talked to him. In a sense he was conscious, but not entirely so. You see he had morphia to save him from the pain. His mind was full of his work, and I am sure he thought he was in a 'plane.

He did not realise how bad he was. But he was very thirsty, and was so grateful for drinks, and always thanked us, and said how sorry he was to be 'such a jolly nuisance.' Towards the end he was quiet under the influence of morphia, and felt no pain at all. Dr Dingley said he would have felt very little and he slowly slipped away to a better place.

He (Dr Dingley) says he has seen several of your son's friends at the Camp, and they told him what a favourite he was, and such a charming fellow to live with and have as a friend. They said too, what lots of kind things he did for all sorts of people without making any fuss about it.

His was a beautiful face, and I am sure he was good, true and knightly.

All our thoughts are with you and your family and on behalf of everyone here may I express our lasting sympathies.

With kindest regards,

Helena Appleton,

Matron, Royal Hampshire Hospital

★ ★ ★

Lt Col JA Chamier, March 21, 1918

Hursley Camp, Winchester

Dear Mr Anderson,

I wanted to write to you to express my sympathy at your loss. You and the Air Force have lost an outstanding young man and he will be sorely missed by all.

Your son had served under me for many months before the accident, and I am not saying 'the usual thing' when I say that I have never known a more efficient Flight Commander. I recommended him for a squadron in November, 1917, and I feel sure he would have had one this year despite his tender age.

Apart from his professional capabilities he was one of the most likeable men I have come into contact with for he had a charm of manner which made him liked by all who knew him. His death was a blow to me, and I can realise to some small degree what you must feel in losing him.

As a pilot he was exceptionally skilled; but accidents in the air are hard to explain, and on the type of machine he was flying a very small slip gets a man into trouble, from which, height is necessary for recovery, and in this case there was no time for action. That he enjoyed life to the last moment and that complete and instantaneous unconsciousness must have made death painless may be a small consolation.

We can ill spare Officers of the type of your son in the Air Force.

With deepest sympathy,

JA Chamier,

Lt Col, RFC

★ ★ ★

Diary of Nora Anderson, March 22, 1918
Glasgow

Yesterday I buried my youngest son. Edward Kerr Anderson. He was 21 and as a man he had known only war and yesterday I buried him a victim of war.

We sang his favourite hymn:

'Clear before us, through the darkness,

Gleams and burns the guiding light;

Brother clasps the hand of brother,

Stepping fearless through the night.'

Oh, Teddie, my Honey Bee. You were so beautiful. You were everything a mother could wish for and now your Flame that burned so bright and bathed everything and everyone you came across in such glorious light is forever extinguished. You lit up the world for the few years that you shared with us. My love for you will never dim and I will remember you always for your goodness and infinite kindness. You have torn our hearts to pieces with your fall.

Dawn is coming and soon I shall open the curtains and watch to see if the sun rises. I have not slept this night. I am weary but I dare not close my eyes as I fear what I may see. If I sleep I do not know if I will ever wake again.

CHAPTER 15

THE LAST

March 22, 1918
The Times, London

GREAT BATTLE OPENED
ATTACKS ON 50-MILE FRONT
ADVANCE INTO BRITISH ZONES
ENEMY'S BIG LOSSES
The War: 4th year: 231st Day.
Three days ago the British Cabinet received information from Headquarters in France that a great German attack was going to be launched immediately. The attack opened yesterday morning, and covered nearly the whole of the British front south from the Scarpe to the Oise, a distance of over 50, miles. It is on a larger scale than any during the war.

Sir Douglas Haig telegraphed last night that the vast attack had been pressed with the greatest vigour throughout the day, and that last night severe fighting continued on the whole front.

The results of the first day's fighting are as follows: – The enemy broke through our outpost positions and succeeded in penetrating into our battle positions in certain parts of the front. The attacks were delivered in large masses, and caused the Germans exceptionally heavy losses. Captured maps show that on no part of the long front of the attack has the enemy obtained his objectives.

DENSE WAVES OF ENEMY INFANTRY
HAND-TO-HAND FIGHTING
War Correspondents' Headquarters,
March 21
At about 5 o'clock this morning the enemy artillery swelled into a heavy

161

bombardment of practically the whole British front south of the Scarpe, and an hour later opened fire with gas shells on the front around Fleurbaix, just south of Armentieres. As I write, at 10 o'clock, the air is thunderous. Our guns are replying strenuously. Thus far no infantry movement is reported. The weather is very hazy and aerial observation is almost impossible.

Our troops are everywhere standing to in readiness for anything that may come along.

LATER – Following the heavy bombardment, the enemy launched an infantry attack on a big scale.

Under cover of a smoke barrage, his infantry came over in dense waves on a front extending from the north of Lagincourt down to Gauche Wood.

At 10.50 a.m. there was hand-to-hand fighting in our front line at various points. The early morning mists had lifted somewhat, and airmen were able to be up. Thus far details coming back from the battle line are scrappy and confused, but it seems certain that the Germans have assumed the offensive on a big scale.

The artillery duel is terrific, more particularly in the region of the ridges about St Quentin, which appear to be a main objective of the German scheme.

The Germans, by employing masses of men, supported by a great weight of artillery, appear to have penetrated our front line at certain spots between the Scarpe and Vendeuil, but it is, as yet, very difficult to state exactly what the position is.

The weather improved during the morning and has been dry and tolerably clear.

* * *

Diary of Nora Anderson, March 23, 1918
Lansdowne Crescent, Glasgow

Still it rains and still I weep for my children. Oh, my Teddie, dear, dear Ted. I pray I gave you a happy life. I see your pictures and they are full of joy. You had a smile that could lift any soul, you stirred spirits and brought a happiness to my simple life. You, darling Ted, were the brightness in my life. Now you are in the cold earth and I am left here mourning another terrible departure.

I do not have the strength to continue. The newspapers are full of terrible things again but I will not look. I sing to myself, nobody can hear me.

Through each perplexing path of life
Our wand'ring footsteps guide;
Give us our day our daily bread,
And rainment fit provide.
O spread Thy covering wings around,
Till all our wand'rings cease,
And at our Father's lov'd abode
Our souls arrive in peace

How the country longs for peace, yet I cannot think I will ever find peace again. I search my mind for a path that might one day lead there, but instead it only takes me backwards.

Dear Ronnie, Sweet Charlie. Innocent, simple boys. They were all mine and all different. It is not how Willie and I planned it should be. It is what they became. Willie used to take photographs of them all together. I have the ones from the golf club at Prestwick. Willie was very proud of them and gave them to me as a present. I have not looked at them for such a while. They are before me now. I have laid them out on the table.

I am not sure which is my favourite. There is one where he lined the boys up against the wall of the club house. Ronnie is the tallest, just outreaching Bertie. I never thought of him as the tallest. I think he was the happiest as it seemed he rarely stopped to think much at all. He does look silly with his pipe, a happy, silly boy, ready for all life's adventures. He treated everything as an adventure. Charlie has a quiet grin, he was such a normal fellow, a true good citizen. He would always try and help. It was always Charlie who offered to lay the table for dinner, especially at Christmas. He so enjoyed helping Lily prepare a festive table, beautifully decorated for all the family. We were all surprised when he settled on the army as his way. I wish he were here to help now.

There was a time before this, that last summer, when Ron was home and the days stretched into slow evenings. Ted and Ron liked to hit golf balls across the lawn. They were still like children for when they thought we 'grown-ups' were not looking they would try and outdo each other by hitting the balls over the trees and out into the field. How that angered poor McCullum. He would seek me out and lay out his complaints and I promised to stop them from tomorrow, make them go down to the course. From tomorrow. I never did.

I wonder how many times over the years McCullum complained to me of the children's activities around his precious garden. Fortune smiled on Willie and I. We were blessed with our children and our home. We could shelter them there as they grew. I did not want even to send them away to school. I wanted Willie to employ a governor to teach them. He thought it was a ridiculous, dated notion, and the expense – dearest Willie is always aware of the expense! and would not consider it. I did not like sending them away, but they made me proud and I am proud of what they became and a mother is allowed to be so. Yet I always longed for summer to come around once more and they would all be home, safe at Strathairly.

Mother would say to me that I had to let them go. I had prepared them for the world and now they had to go out into it and find themselves as men. A mother's strings have to be cut. She said that often to me. I did as she said, for I thought she was right, but now I wish I had kept them here.

I look at Teddie in the photographs and I know I am going to weep again. When will I ever stop weeping?

I want my Bertie back. Dear God, I have asked for so very little because I have had so very much. For this one time, grant my prayers I beg of you, Merciful Father. Bring my Bertie back to me. He is all I have.

★ ★ ★

March 23, 1918
The Times, London

GREAT BATTLE RENEWED
"SOME PROGRESS BY THE ENEMY"
A GALLANT DEFENCE
The War: 4th year; 232nd Day.
Over half a million of the enemy are trying to burst through the British lines on a front of nearly 60 miles in France. The ground on

which this battle, the greatest since the Marne, is being fought is on the downs between the Somme, Scarpe, and Oise, devastated in the German retreat to the Hindenburg line a year ago. Ordering a defensive until the downfall of Russia released the bulk of German armies for use in the West, Hindenburg is now throwing Germany's main military strength into one gigantic struggle in the hope of final victory.

The battle has now been waged for two days. By Thursday night part of our forces had been forced back by weight of numbers to their reserve line, and troops who had held their ground at other points were withdrawn to conform with the new line of defence.

After a quiet period the struggle was renewed with vigour yesterday morning along practically the whole front. The general situation was that the enemy had made some progress at certain points and had been thrown back at others by counter-attack. Our losses had inevitably been considerable, but the enemy's continued to be very heavy.

"Our troops are fighting with the greatest gallantry," Sir Douglas Haig says. "Further fighting of the most severe nature is anticipated."

★ ★ ★

Diary of Nora Anderson, March 24, 1918
Lansdowne Crescent, Glasgow

It was already raining when I woke this morning and there was a chill to the air. Spring is still far away. Willie was not up when I rose. He is tired again. We have not spoken much. I do not believe there is anything that we can say to each other. They would only be words and words cannot heal.

I made some porridge, enough for Willie too, and it was comforting to taste its warmth. I will warm it again when Willie rises. He needs to eat more. He looks as if he is wasting away.

I have left my door open so I will hear if he is about. I need to care for him. I feel tired too and I have much to do today, altho I do not care for going forth in this rain. Perhaps I shall wait until after lunch.

★ ★ ★

March 25, 1918
The Times, London

BACK TO THE SOMME
BRITISH ARMIES ON THE DEFENSIVE
PERONNE AND HAM LOST
The War: 4th year: 234th Day.
Before the masses of German troops on the long front from the Scarpe to the Oise the British forces have retreated to the Somme on the southern part of their front. For two days they had, before overwhelming numbers, fallen back slowly, full of fight, and had taken a tremendous toll of the enemy.

Then west of St Quentin a breach was made in their lines, and a larger and quicker withdrawal became necessary.

Our armies now roughly hold a line running due south from the Scarpe, reaching the Somme near Peronne. Thus about two-thirds of the country evacuated by the enemy over a year ago has been lost, and a withdrawal of 15 miles made at one point.

The battle continued with the greatest intensity yesterday, the fourth day of the German onslaught. The enemy is converging on the old Somme battlefield from Bapaume to Peronne. Peronne has been lost, but further north the defence is holding out finely. To the south the troops who fell back after the break west of St Quentin hold in the main the line of the river to a point near the town of Ham.

THE 50-MILE BATTLE
SPLENDID BRITISH RESISTANCE
BATTALIONS MEET DIVISIONS
From Our Special Correspondent.

March 24 – The great battle continues to rage with unabated violence, and the British troops are fighting, I believe, as splendidly as they fought in the first great clashes of this war – or as ever in their history.

It is true that the Germans continue to press on. They have recovered all the ground which they lost in the Cambrai battle, and are now gradually recovering portions of the area they left when they retreated after their defeat on the Somme. But their losses are terrific.

Instead of the break which the enemy anticipated, our line is firm and continuous everywhere before him, and, so far from having any

166

notion of being a beaten Army, our men in their moral remain magnificent.

The German gains are large, but we know that they had counted on getting by this time from three times to five times farther than they have actually got. We are unshaken in front of them.

As for the fighting of our men, I have no forms of praise sufficient. The battle has seen a thousand Thermopylaes and every officer's voice rings with pride when he speaks of the behaviour of his men.

You will understand that it is not easy to give a connected account of the details of a conflict of such enormous scope.

Every hour the situation changes, and the great line sways and reels as, at one point or another, the Germans force a new penetration or we hurl them back again from ground they thought they won.

When the second night fell our line then ran behind Henin Hill through Mory and Vaulx-Vraucourt. Late that night great new masses of Germans came moving forward and all through the night the struggle raged without cessation.

In the early morning we pushed forward again, Scottish and English troops together, drove the Germans back and extraordinarily confused fighting went on through yesterday with the two lines mixed up and bodies of one or other side between the positions of the other. When evening fell we drew back to a continuous and prepared line further west.

Here, as elsewhere along the front, the story is one of heroic fighting whilst gradually falling back. What the German losses have been on this part of the front is impossible to guess, but I believe it is no exaggeration to say that if we had lost every man engaged on our side it would not have equalled the enemy casualties. That, certainly, is the opinion of all our men engaged or in a position to know.

"A WONDERFUL GOOD SHOW"

I have talked to-day with men who were in the fighting here and saw or took part in the counter-attacks. So jubilant were they at what they called the "wonderful good show" and the fighting of our men that they could hardly tell of it coherently.

We have faced fearful odds against us, and our losses were inevitably heavy. Yet though physically worn-out, almost to the point of collapse, the men positively crowed with joy when they told of the fighting and how they had made the Germans suffer. Never have I been more profoundly *impressed with the quality of our men. The Germans are paying a bitter price for every foot of ground they win, and everywhere our men, however tired with fighting, almost sometimes to the point of physical exhaustion, are full of heart and confidence. The weather, though misty in the first day's battle, is now beautiful and worthy of Palm Sunday.*

★ ★ ★

Diary of Nora Anderson, March 26, 1918
Lansdowne Crescent, Glasgow

When the Lord shall summon us
Whom thou hast left behind,
May we, untainted by the world,
As sure a welcome find;
May each, like thee, depart in peace,
To be a glorious guest,
Where the wicked cease from troubling,
And the weary are at rest.
Amen

★ ★ ★

March 26, 1918
The Times, London

NEW SOMME BATTLES
THE THRUST FROM THE NORTH
BAPAUME LOST
The War: 4th Year: 235th Day.
"Our troops, though tired, are in good heart, and are fighting splendidly, and the enemy is only progressing at the cost of heavy sacrifices." The War Office in these words summed up the position of the great battle early last night. Later Sir Douglas Haig telegraphed that the enemy were attacking north and south with fresh forces, and that, in spite of gallant resistance, our troops had been compelled to give ground.

"The Empire stands calm and confident in its soldiers." The King thus expresses the national feelings in a message to Sir Douglas Haig.

GREAT DAYS OF STRUGGLE

From Our Special Correspondent

March 25 – The battle continues without slackening along the whole great front. The Germans have made more progress, but nowhere is that progress comparable with their aims or their expectations. Everywhere they are faced still by the line which bends and sags and seems to yield, but is always there, confronting them.

In moving, as a correspondent must, behind the lines, I have been impressed with nothing so much as with the cool, orderly determination of our men. Their manner and speech are eloquent of confidence in themselves.

Those who go up to the line know what is ahead of them, and they go up laughing and tossing jests about. Those who come out, weary, bedraggled (Oh! how weary and bedraggled I have seen some of them!), are full of fire and dogged pride. They have fallen or been ordered back, but … then comes the tale of how they have dealt with the enemy and the tale is everywhere the same. The German losses, are beyond doubt, enormous.

A very stubborn struggle is also going on along the course of the Somme about Peronne and south of there, where for 36 hours the Germans have been making tremendous efforts to cross the river and strike westward.

The enemy pressed all night, and in the morning the struggle was resumed at the fiercest and then it was that at Le Verguier a body of the Queen's West Surreys held out and fought to literally, as it is believed, the last man. On the right of Le Verguier itself the struggle was no less intense, nor less glorious; it went on towards Caubrieres Wood, and here and again at Vendrecourt Chateau the losses inflicted on the enemy were very heavy, our infantry and machine-gunners alike being almost worn out with killing till arms and bodies ached.

★ ★ ★

April 2, 1918
Post Office Telegraphs, Glasgow

To: Secretary, War Office, London
Hear report my son Lieut Col WH Anderson 12th HLI killed on 25th March.

Is this true?

From: Anderson, 14 Lansdowne Cresct, Glasgow

★ ★ ★

April 3, 1918
Post Office Telegraphs, London

To: Anderson, 14 Lansdowne Crescent, Glasgow
In response to your wire No report of any recent casualty to Lt Col WH
ANDERSON Highland Light Infantry received at War Office.
From: SECRETARY, WAR OFFICE

★ ★ ★

Diary of Nora Anderson, April 4, 1918
Strathairly

I am sitting in my bedroom for it affords the best view over the gate
and so I shall see the telegram boy at once.

He is coming. It may be today, tomorrow or the next day, but he will
come and he will hand that brown envelope to Lily and she shall take it
to Willie and in time Willie will come up here. I will hear his slow, heavy
tread on the stairs and then I shall know from his face as he opens the
door that our last son is gone.

I know he is gone. The father of one of his men in the battalion had
news from his son, who himself had been wounded. He came to see
Willie and they went into the study and closed the door. He was here
for ten minutes and after he left Willie told me. The life has gone out of
him.

They have them all now. My boys. In the Highlands it is called 'Tir
nan Og', the land of the young. Reverend Stuart calls it The Better
Place.

I pray that it is.

★ ★ ★

April 5, 1918
Post Office Telegraphs, London

To: Mrs Anderson, Woodbank, Balloch, Dumbartonshire
Deeply regret Lieut Col WH ANDERSON Highland Light Infantry killed
in Action March twenty fifth. The Army Council express their sympathy.
    From: SECRETARY WAR OFFICE

CHAPTER 16

REMAINS

The following unfinished letter was found among Bertie's belongings:

March 22, 1918
France

My darling G,

How do you live on when so much has gone, your body withering, your mind clutching at sacred memories that will fade no matter the polishing?

My body aches, tiredness assaults me, but I will go on because I want to see my dear wife and sons again. It is my duty now to survive. John Cox said as we marched up that I would be sent home once this particular struggle is settled as our family has served its due. That is what happens apparently when you reach the very edge of hell, you are spared. Spared what? My darling, I will not leave. I can not. You know that, as dear Gertie you know how true my love for you remains. I am yours always.

When the news reached me, I saw him. He will never grow old

★ ★ ★

May 3, 1918
London Gazette Supplement

The King has been pleased to approve the award of the Victoria Cross to the following Officer: – T/Maj. (A/Lt-Col) William Herbert Anderson, late HLI.

For most conspicuous bravery, determination, and gallant leading of his command.

The enemy attacked on the right of the battalion frontage and succeeded in penetrating the wood held by our men. Owing to successive lines of the enemy following on closely, there was the gravest danger that the flank would be turned. Grasping the seriousness of the situation, Colonel Anderson made his way across the open in full view of the enemy now holding the wood on the right, and after much effort succeeded in gathering the remainder of the two right companies. He personally led the counter-attack and drove the enemy from the wood, capturing 12 machine-guns and 70 prisoners, and restoring the original line.

His conduct in leading the charge was quite fearless, and his most splendid example was the means of rallying and inspiring the men during a most critical hour.

Later on the same day, in another position, the enemy had penetrated to within 300 yards of the village and were holding a timber-yard in force. Colonel Anderson reorganised his men and brought them forward to a position of readiness for a counter-attack. He led the attack and throughout showed the utmost disregard for his own safety. The counter-attack drove the enemy from his position, but resulted in this very gallant officer losing his life. He died fighting within the enemy's lines, setting a magnificent example to all who were privileged to serve under him.

★ ★ ★

January 23, 1920
Glasgow Herald

ANDERSON MEMORIAL UNVEILING
IN GLASGOW CATHEDRAL
A mural tablet to the memory of the four sons of Mr WJ Anderson who lost their lives in the war was unveiled yesterday afternoon in Glasgow Cathedral.

The tablet is in bronze and is of chaste design. The inscription bears that it is "to the memory of four brothers, natives of this city, who died for their country and in the cause of honour and freedom."

They were: – Captain Charles Hamilton Anderson, Highland Light Infantry; Lieutenant Alexander Ronald Anderson, Highland Light Infantry; Captain Edward Kerr Anderson, Royal Flying

Corps; and Lieut-Colonel William Herbert Anderson, VC, Highland Light Infantry.

In performing the ceremony, Mr Alan F Baird said he had the great honour of unveiling that memorial. It had fallen to him, as an old friend, to recall something of what they were. In doing so, he would not dwell on the tragedy in which has swept away a generation. He knew that it would be the feeling of those nearest to them that little should be said of the extent of the loss. Words were poor and weak in the presence of tragedy. But it was right that they should recall something of the brothers.

The first to depart this life was Captain Charles Hamilton Anderson, whom many of them must remember as a gay debonair young soldier whose great charm of manner did not conceal his devotion to duty. His brief warfare was soon accomplished.

Next to follow was his brother Alexander Ronald, affectionately known as "Ronnie", for he had many friends and, indeed, he was, in the words of Scripture, a choice young man and goodly and anointed with the oil of gladness above his fellows.

After him came the youngest brother. Edward Kerr Anderson. Him they knew as a charming lad. But what they were not prepared to learn was that this little more than schoolboy developed into one of the most intrepid and skilful of that daring band of young men they knew as the Royal Flying Corps. Fighting on the Somme, he (Mr Baird) remembered that he wrote home that after a successful flight he had come back singing for very joy. "His glory, like a shooting star, fell to the base earth."

Last of the four and the eldest of all was Colonel William Herbert Anderson, VC. He and his brothers gave all they could, but from one point of view he had most to give, for he had wife and children, had friends, had an honourable place and career before him, had everything that life could offer, and he gave them all.

Mr Baird had spoken of these splendid men individually, but while one remembered each of them one could not but think of them as a band of brothers. "Amabiles et decori in vita nec in morte sua divisi sunt."

Indeed, the words of the Vulgate, which he had quoted, were considered as part of the inscription, but it was thought that the line chosen was more apt in testifying to their gratitude. It read – "Happy

174

is he who thinks the safety and liberty of many well bought at the cost of his own life."

They gallantly and cheerfully paid the price of our safety and our liberty, and now "from the contagion of the world's slow stain" they were secure. It had been a small matter, but a labour of love, to raise that tablet to them, and to feel that it would long after this recall the memory of these four brothers and tell the citizens of Glasgow of a very great and perfect sacrifice.

★ ★ ★

January 13, 1922
Glasgow Herald

DEATH OF WELL-KNOWN GLASGOW STOCKBROKER

The death was announced yesterday of Mr WJ Anderson, CBE, a well-known Glasgow stockbroker, in his Fifeshire home.

He was in Glasgow on Wednesday, when he appeared to be in his usual health.

Mr Anderson was, before retiring, associated with the one-time firm of Messrs Kerr, Andersons and MacLeod, and was 70 years of age. He was secretary of the Scottish Red Cross, and during the war lost four sons.

★ ★ ★

Diary of Nora Anderson, January 16, 1922
Strathairly

William was buried yesterday afternoon. This afternoon the sun is shining. All the way back from Glasgow this morning I watched it trying to force back the clouds. It did not try yesterday.

I can hear voices from downstairs. Someone is in the hall, my dear old Lily I think. The motor from Glasgow must have arrived. They wanted me to travel with them but I wanted to return to Strathairly at once. I will not ever leave here again.

I can hear the children's voices now. They must be outside on the lawn, playing in the sun just as mine used to. I have my album on my lap. I never am without it and if I opened it I could see pictures of Them on the lawn.

Strathairly may sound alive, yet I cannot feel it. I cannot feel very much at all. I do not feel for William. I think we both died four years ago. When I watched his coffin lowered into Scotland's dark earth it was a moment of envy. I am not afraid of dying, it must be better than this emptiness that is consuming me. Every day another piece of me yields to its darkness.

Oh Willie, my husband, where have you gone? Are you marching proudly alongside Charlie, Ronnie, poor Bertie and my darling young Teddie? If you are then you are in step with the angels. My angels.

POSTSCRIPT

Charlie's body was never found; he is one of 13,000 such unknowns commemorated on the Le Touret Memorial in the Pas de Calais. A few miles away Ronnie is buried in the Cabaret-Rouge British Cemetery. Bertie lies not far from where he was killed, in the Peronne Road Cemetery outside Maricourt on the Somme. Teddie made it home. His body was brought back to Scotland and buried in New Kilpatrick Parish churchyard in Glasgow. A plaque dedicated to the brothers remains today in the west wing of Glasgow cathedral.

Nora Anderson died at Strathairly in 1939. She was 79.

Gertie died at the age of 82 in 1967. She never remarried.

Bertie's sons, Charlie and Allan, both joined the army and survived the Second World War. Allan died in 1972, Charlie in 1998. Charlie was my grandfather.